Loss and Expense Explained

Loss and Expense Explained

Paul Newman and Jeff Whitfield

Published by RIBA Publications,
the publishing division of RIBA Companies Ltd,
Finsbury Mission, 39 Moreland Street, London EC1V 8BB

ISBN 185 946 001 1

Editor: Alaine Hamilton
Book design and computer page make-up: Penny Mills
Printed and bound by Biddles Ltd, Guildford

Contents

Preface

Three enduring features of the construction industry are conflict, claims and claims resolution. Architects, encouraged perhaps by the methodology of certain claims consultants, tend to believe that claims are *de facto* invalid and simply represent an attempt on the part of the contractor to get one over on the architect. However, all the standard form contracts make specific provision for the contractor to be paid additional monies in certain prescribed circumstances, and the common law has developed a similar series of remedies for the contractor who genuinely incurs costs over and above those which he could reasonably build into his original tender.

Loss and Expense Explained, jointly written by a lawyer and a quantity surveyor, seeks to describe the legal framework for claims in the construction industry and provide practical guidance about the way claims should be set out and negotiated. The book is addressed primarily to architects and others acting as contract administrators and/or project managers, but it will be found useful and relevant by clients, developers, contractors, sub-contractors, claims consultants and quantity surveyors.

There are a number of people to whom the authors would like to express their thanks. At Edwards Geldard, these include the practice librarian, Mary Michell, and Personal Assistant, Diane Smith. At Stapletons, they include Managing Director and proof reader, David Sloan, and long-suffering secretary, Barbara Metcalfe. We are also grateful to other professional colleagues and associates for their comments on various chapters of the book when in draft. We especially thank John Redmond of Laytons, Bristol; Peter McCartney of Contract and Construction Consultants Ltd, Bristol; Professor Michael Furmston of Bristol University for providing transcripts of *Ogilvie Builders Ltd v Glasgow City Council* and *R.W. Miller & Co Pty Ltd v Krupp (Australia) Pty Ltd*; and Philip Harvey, whose comments on the text were as incisive as expected.

Our final thanks are due to our Editor, Alaine Hamilton, Stanley Cox of the Welsh School of Architecture, Cardiff, our respective wives, Veronica and Susan, and our families.

Paul Newman, Cardiff
Jeff Whitfield, Darlington
October 1994

POSTSCRIPT

Since the main part of the text was completed, Mr Peter Aeberli of 199, The Strand, London, has provided a further slant on global claims with the transcript of the unreported Australian case, *Naura Phosphate Royalties Trust v Matthew Hall Mechanical* and *Electrical Engineers Pty Ltd and Richard Butterworth*. An analysis of this Australian decision by Mr Aeberli is to be found in *Arbitration and Dispute Resolution Law Journal* at [1993] ADRLJ 223.

The issue of head office overheads and what is required to ensure their recovery was considered by His Honour Judge Humphrey Lloyd QC, Official Referee, in *Babcock Energy Ltd v Lodge Sturtevant Ltd*, 28 July 1994 (unreported). There is a useful résumé of the case by Vincent Powell-Smith in *Contract Journal* of 8–14 September 1994.

Glossary, definitions and abbreviations

Readers may not be familiar with some of the legal terminology used in the book. Generally, when a term is first employed an explanation is included in the text. Some non-legal words are used for a particular sense in the book, and a definition is therefore included here.

ACAS: Advisory Conciliation and Arbitration Service.

Adjudication: An informal method of challenging decisions (especially set-offs) and resolving disputes under certain main and sub-contract forms without recourse to litigation or arbitration.

Adjudicator: The person under certain main and sub-contract forms to whom specified disputes are referred for consideration.

Affidavit: A written statement the contents of which are confirmed to be true and accurate under Oath. Used to substantiate various formal applications to the courts.

Alternative Dispute Resolution (ADR): An umbrella term to describe methods of dispute resolution other than arbitration or litigation. Although there are many hybrids, the usual methods are mediation, conciliation and the mini-trial. ADR is usually non-binding.

Arbitration: A binding method of dispute resolution common under standard form building and engineering contracts where disputes are referred to an independent arbitrator. If the parties have a written agreement to arbitrate their disputes, the arbitration is conducted in accordance with the Arbitration Acts 1950–1979.

Arbitrator: The person appointed either by agreement of the parties or by an appointing body (eg the RIBA or RICS) to decide disputes referred to him by the parties in accordance with the rules and procedures of arbitration.

Articles of Agreement: The operative part of a contract which defines the rights and obligations of the parties. Often the Articles of Agreement are prefaced by the words 'Now it is hereby agreed as follows' or similar.

Balance of probabilities: The standard of proof required of a plaintiff in non-criminal cases to substantiate his claim.

Banwell Report:	A report into the construction industry and its practices published in 1964. Also known more formally as the report of the 'Committee on the Placing and Management of Contracts for Building and Civil Engineering Work'.
Base date:	The date stated in the contract appendix for the operation of certain contract clauses, eg fluctuations.
Case law:	The previous reported decisions of the courts which either bind other judges or have persuasive authority in the resolution of disputes.
Causation:	The requirement on party A to demonstrate that a particular act or omission of party B is directly responsible for loss or damage to party A.
Centre for Dispute Resolution (CEDR):	An independent body, based in London, which was set up in 1990 to promote and oversee the development of ADR in the UK.
Chartered Institute of Arbitrators (CIArb):	A body, based in London, which is responsible for the training of arbitrators and the propagation of information about arbitration law.
Claimant:	The party who brings a legal case as arbitration proceedings. In litigation such a party is known as the plaintiff.
Claims consultant:	A person (often a quantity surveyor) who specialises in the preparation and presentation of loss and expense claims and may appear as an expert witness in arbitration or litigation.
Common law:	The system of law which has its historic roots in the common customs of the country. It is not based upon legislation or equity (principles of law based upon discretion and conscience) but upon case law.
Condition precedent:	A specific event which must come about prior to a particular situation occurring.
Contra proferentem:	A Latin term meaning 'against the person putting [it] forward'. It is a rule of law adopted when considering a contract which contains an ambiguity of wording. The contract is interpreted against the interests of the person drawing it up, or who would benefit from it.
Contract Bills:	An abbreviation of bills of quantities (also known as bills) which provide the description, often in several volumes, of the works to be carried out and which will be priced by the contractor.

County Court: The court in England and Wales which ordinarily deals with contract and tort claims to a value not exceeding £50,000.

Court of Appeal: The court which hears appeals from the High Court and the County Court.

Critical path: The sequence of stages in a building programme which must follow each other sequentially, each of which depends on the completion of the previous stage, and all of which are essential in order to achieve practical completion by the date for completion.

Cross-examination: The process by which a plaintiff's witnesses are asked questions by the defendant's representative and vice versa.

Culpable overrun: A contractor is in culpable overrun or delay when the contractual completion date has passed without practical completion having been achieved, and the contract administrator does not consider that the contractor is entitled to a further extension of time.

Dayworks: A method of payment for building works where the hours worked by each operative and materials used are agreed. Payment will contain a further element for overheads and profit.

Defence: The name applied to the document in High Court or County Court proceedings in which the defendant responds to the plaintiff's case against him. In arbitration this document is referred to as 'the Points of Defence'.

Directive: A type of European legislation which outlines the objective to be achieved in member states of the European Union but leaves the method of implementation to member states.

Discovery: The stage in litigation or arbitration at which each party informs the other, usually in the form of a written list, of the documents he possesses which relate to the dispute.

Evidence in Chief: The oral or written evidence given by witnesses in arbitration or litigation prior to cross-examination.

Expert witness: A suitably qualified or experienced third party retained by the plaintiff or defendant to provide opinion evidence on the facts of a case.

Extension of time: The provision of an extended period to the contractor to complete the contract works for one or more of a number of prescribed reasons where the contractor has not caused the delay.

Financing charges: The cost of a contractor being kept out of his monies which is not claimed as interest for late payment of a debt but as a constituent element of the contractor's loss and expense.

Final Account: The sum calculated as due and owing to the contractor in regard to the contract works as a whole on completion.

Float: The period in a contractor's programme which he does not anticipate will be required for completion of the contract works.

Fluctuations: Adjustments to the contract sum to take account of increases or decreases in the cost of the works.

Further and Better Particulars: A procedure used in arbitration and litigation to elicit further information from the other party about the contents of a particular pleading.

Global claims: A method of calculating a contractor's loss and expense by allocating a single sum to all the factors of delay rather than assessing accurately the loss attributable to a particular delay.

Head Office overheads: The financial return a contractor requires from a particular contract to assist the funding of his business as a whole.

High Court: Comprised of two sections, the Queen's Bench Division and the Chancery Division, the work of which is often interchangeable. Sits in London and major regional centres and deals with the more complex cases outside the expertise of the County Court.

House of Lords: The highest court in England and Wales which hears appeals from the Court of Appeal.

Inspection: Occurs after discovery and is the formal inspection by each party of the other's documents.`

Judgment: The binding and final decision of the judge in legal proceedings. In arbitration this is described as 'the Award'.

Judgment in default: In court proceedings a plaintiff may obtain 'default' judgment if a defence is not submitted within prescribed time limits.

Liquidated and ascertained damages: A 'genuine pre-estimate' of loss which will be occasioned by a particular breach of contract. Found in standard form building contracts to compensate the employer for the contractor's inability to finish building works during the contract period.

Main contractor's discount:	The percentage reduction (usually 2½% but often now as much as 4%) due to a main contractor for prompt payment to sub-contractors.
Mitigation of loss:	The obligation on a party who has suffered a breach of contract reasonably to reduce as much as possible financial losses caused by the breach of contract.
NEDO formula:	One of the published indices relating to inflation.
Negligence:	One of the sub-divisions of the law of tort.
Obiter [dictum]:	The part of a judgment which is not strictly relevant to the issues in dispute in a case.
Official Referee:	A judge who specialises in hearing technical cases, particularly building and engineering cases.
Order 14:	See Summary Judgment.
Pleadings:	A generic term used to describe the documentation prepared by the parties in litigation or arbitration to set out their respective cases.
Points of Claim:	The document in arbitration proceedings in which the claimant sets out his case. This document is known in High Court proceedings as 'the Statement of Claim' and in County Court proceedings as 'the Particulars of Claim'.
Preliminaries:	The costs resulting from work, materials or facilities ancillary to but necessary for the carrying out of the contract works.
Prime cost sums:	Sums inserted in bills of quantities against nominated sub-contractor work.
Provisional sum:	An item in the bills of quantities for work yet to be fully detailed or described.
Quantum meruit:	A reasonable valuation of work undertaken. It generally applies when a payment (or the method for calculating it) has not been specified or there is no contract in existence but the circumstances demand that a fair valuation is carried out.
Respondent:	The term used in arbitration proceedings to refer to the party who is sued. In litigation the party sued is known as the defendant.
Rolled-up claims:	See global claims.
Rules of the Supreme Court:	Known as 'the White Book'. The procedures for bringing cases in the High Court.

Set-off: Set-off takes a number of forms but it can be generally described as a method by which a defendant seeks to reduce a claim against him by bringing into account monies owed to him by the plaintiff.

Special damages: Damages which are particular to the plaintiff and would not ordinarily have been incurred by other plaintiffs in similar circumstances.

Statements of Case: Documents often used in arbitration proceedings in which the claimant and respondent set out their cases in the form of a detailed narrative which incorporates and exhibits other documents upon which they rely.

Summary judgment: Judgment made in either the County Court or the High Court without a full trial where the court is satisfied that the defendant does not have an arguable case. In the High Court summary judgment is sometimes known as Order 14, which is the specific rule of the High Court under which summary judgment applications are made.

Summons: A procedural document necessary for the making of certain applications to the courts.

Tort: A civil wrong distinct from contract law.

Total loss claims: See global claims.

Variation: A change to or modification of the contract works required by the employer or architect on his behalf.

Writ: The document used in High Court proceedings to commence a plaintiff's case.

Abbreviations

Main contract forms

ACA Edition 2:   Association of Consultant Architects Form of Building Agreement 1982 (Second Edition 1984, 1990 Revision).

CD 81:   Joint Contracts Tribunal Standard Form of Building Contract With Contractor's Design (1981 Edition).

GC/Works/1:   General Conditions of Government Contract for Building and Civil Engineering. Currently in Edition 3.

FIDIC: Fédération Internationale des Ingénieurs-Conseils, a standard form contract for civil engineering (usually international) projects. Currently in 4th Edition.

ICE: Institution of Civil Engineers Conditions of Contract for use in connection with Works of Civil Engineering Construction (approved by ICE, ACE and FCEC). Currently in 6th Edition.

IFC 84:   Joint Contracts Tribunal Intermediate Form of Building Contract (1984 Edition).

JCT 63:   Joint Contracts Tribunal Standard Form Building Contract (1963 Edition). No longer published. Sometimes encountered in the 1977 Revision.

JCT 80:   Joint Contracts Tribunal Standard Form Building Contract (1980 Edition).

MW 80:   Joint Contracts Tribunal Agreement for Minor Works (1980 Edition).

Sub-contract forms

DOM/1:   BEC/FASS/CASEC Form of Domestic Sub-contract for use with JCT 80.

DOM/2:   BEC/FASS/CASEC Form of Domestic Sub-contract for use with CD 81.

NAM/SC: Sub-contract for use with IFC 84 where the sub-contractor is named.

NSC/C: JCT Form of Nominated Sub-contract for use with JCT 80 (previously NSC/4 or NSC/4a)

Professional organisations

ACA:	Association of Consultant Architects.
ACE:	Association of Consulting Engineers.
BEC:	Building Employers Confederation.
CASEC:	Confederation of Associations of Specialist Engineering Contractors
FASS:	Federation of Associations of Specialist and Sub-contractors.
FCEC:	Federation of Civil Engineering Contractors.
FIDIC:	Fédération Internationale des Ingénieurs-Conseils.
ICE:	Institution of Civil Engineers.
JCT:	Joint Contracts Tribunal.
RIBA:	Royal Institute of British Architects.
RICS:	Royal Institution of Chartered Surveyors.

Law reports

AC:	Appeal Cases.
All ER:	All England Reports.
ALJR:	Australian Law Journal Reports.
BLR:	Building Law Reports.
CILL:	Construction Industry Law Letter.
Ch:	Chancery Division.
CLD:	Construction Law Digest.
Con LR:	Construction Law Reports.
Const LJ:	Construction Law Journal.
DLR:	Dominion Law Reports.
Exch.:	Exchequer.
KB:	King's Bench.
Lloyd's Rep:	Lloyd's Reports.
LT:	The Law Times Reports.
NY:	New York.
PD:	Probate Division.
The Times:	Times Newspaper.
WLR:	Weekly Law Reports.

Table of Statutes

Administration of Justice Act 1982

Arbitration Act 1950

Arbitration Act 1975

Arbitration Act 1979

Judgment Act 1839

Law Reform (Contributory Negligence) Act 1945

Law Reform (Miscellaneous Provisions) Act 1934

Sale of Goods Act 1979

Supply of Goods and Services Act 1982

Supreme Court Act 1981

Unfair Contract Terms Act 1977

Unfair Contract Terms in Consumer Contracts 93/13/EEC

1 Introduction

1.01 Complex construction projects often take a considerable time to complete; some require many months and some need years. Within such a prolonged contract period the need for change in the design is bound to arise, along with the occurrence of other delaying factors. The authors of the standard form contracts do their best to anticipate and provide for all possible events as well as consider and draft amendments either made necessary or desirable as a result of judicial interpretation of particular clauses. Even with these amendments included the contract terms inevitably fall short of perfection. Sooner or later an event or series of events will transpire that falls outside the scope of the contract, or the judges will give a new and unexpected twist to the meaning of a particular provision. The occurrence of the former will cause the affected party, usually the contractor, to seek additional remuneration by way of damages to take account of the changed circumstances. Where a disruptive event is anticipated by the contract, for example where delay in the provision of design information causes the contractor to incur a loss, the contractor will seek reimbursement under the contract. In all these situations where the contractor seeks additional monies the document produced to encourage the employer to reimburse the contractor for the loss is called a 'claim'. However, 'claim' is generic, descriptively vague and imprecise. So what does it mean?

1.02 The word 'claim' is used to describe two different types of request that are more appropriately described as:

- an application for reimbursement of, in JCT parlance, direct loss and/or expense arising from a clause in the contract that creates such an entitlement; or
- a claim for damages arising from a breach, or a series of breaches, of the contract conditions.

The two different types of claim are often inextricably linked together.

1.03 The frequent overlapping of breaches and contractual entitlements is best explained by an example that is by no means uncommon. A contractor was delayed by a late issue of design information and as such was entitled to recompense for his costs under the contract conditions. In the same period the employer was himself unable to give access to the land, which had been occupied by itinerants. As there was no contract clause allowing for the deferment of the date for possession of the land, this was considered to be a breach of contract by the employer for which the contractor could seek common law damages. In circumstances such as these, as well as in many others, it is almost inevitable that the resulting claims will encompass loss and expense and damages.

1.04   Unfortunately, understanding how claims arise does not necessarily provide a complete understanding of why claims arise. Legitimate claims are raised where there are breaches of contract and/or entitlements under the contract. There are a number of other reasons why spurious claims may be forwarded to their employers by contractors and sub-contractors. It is important to identify the purpose of such claims so that the wheat can be sifted from the chaff. There are three main reasons for submitting a claim that is later shown to be unfounded or invalid. These are briefly examined below.

1.05   The first is arguably the most common. There are genuine grounds for a claim of one type or another but, unfortunately, adequate contemporary records have not been kept. In these circumstances it is not unusual to find that contractors have acted on oral instructions or even on their own initiative, believing this course of action to be in the best interests of the project. Alternatively, they may have been issued with properly documented instructions or granted extensions of time but have failed to keep records of the resulting losses. In either case the claim will be evidentially weak and the claimant may have to resort to submitting an unparticularised, global or rolled-up claim. Such claims are considered in Section 5.

1.06   The second reason for an apparently spurious claim to be made is that the contractor has genuinely incurred a loss on the project and wishes to have his losses made good, thus putting himself back into the profitable situation he fondly imagines he enjoyed the prospect of at tender stage. In many instances the contractor cannot be certain why losses have arisen, but he is quite certain that he did not cause them. Unfortunately for the contractor there are many examples of how a loss could very easily be laid at his own door, including inadequate tender provisions, low site productivity, poor supervision, inadequate supply of labour and materials and the effect of price escalation on labour, materials and sub-contracts. Unless the contractor can properly demonstrate that his losses have arisen due to the acts or omissions of his employer his case must fail.

1.07   The third reason for the submission of a speculative claim by a contractor is, quite simply, greed. In some instances an architect or employer's representative is perceived as being weak and as a result he may be pressurised into being too permissive in the granting of instructions and extensions of time. On other occasions public bodies are seen as money wells from which extra cash can be drawn at will. Certain contractors may perceive some public and private concerns as publicity-shy; a notable example is the nuclear industry. Such contractors deliberately press their claims to arbitration or litigation knowing that the employer will settle rather than face the glare of the broadly unsympathetic media. In each case the claimant intends to improve his financial position beyond that which is contractually proper.

1.08   On the other hand, employers may subject the architect or the supervising officer to intense pressure, encouraging him to reduce payments or refuse extensions of time. Architects, annoyed at such improper tactics, act on their conscience and in strict accordance with the law only to find that the employer is slow to honour their certificates and is generally obstructive in regard to any attempt to administer the contract properly. It is not unknown for employers and contractors to starve financially weak companies of cash flow deliberately in the hope that these companies will be in no position to fight for their proper entitlements later. Sadly these tactics occasionally do succeed but they also create disruptive and expensive conflict.

1.09   Conflict in the construction industry is costly and the need to resolve it diverts vital project management effort away from the successful completion of the project. A serious conflict could easily add 20% or more to a project's final cost. Absolute honesty in making claims and in responding to them will do much to reduce the potential for conflict. Some conflict in the prosecution and defence of a claim is inevitable because of hostile personalities, incompatible goals and the different understandings placed upon the contract wording, but most of it can be alleviated by adopting a polite, respectful and even-handed approach to the differences between the parties. A greater use of partnering, both pre-contract and during the currency of a contract can also reduce conflict. This subject is covered in some detail by Jeff Whitfield in *Conflicts in Construction – Avoiding, Managing, Resolving* (MacMillan, 1994).

1.10 In summary, claims can be submitted in response to contractual or extra-contractual events. They may be legitimate or spurious, but into whichever category they fall, they must be taken seriously and properly administered.

2 The architect as certifier – he who pays the piper calls the tune?

2.01   In his December 1993 Interim Report on the future of the construction industry, *Trust and Money*, Sir Michael Latham stated at paragraph 42(2):

> 'The architectural profession [however], takes the view that JCT 80 is specifically drafted in terms which lay the professional duty of impartial contract administration upon the architect ...'

2.02   Traditional building and civil engineering contracts of the JCT and ICE types are drafted in terms that the employer engages the contractor to carry out the works with the architect or engineer as contract administrator. Not a party to the contract, the architect or engineer nevertheless oversees all aspects of contract administration, including the valuation of measured work and variations, ascertainment of the contractor's entitlement to loss and expense (however described) and the assessment of extensions of time. Under the JCT standard form of contract, JCT 80, the architect or contract administrator, appointed by the employer and named in Article 2, either ascertains loss and expense himself and carries out valuations, or delegates these responsibilities to the quantity surveyor. Nowadays delegation is usual and is anticipated by Clauses 26·1, 26·1·2 and 30·1·2 of JCT 80. Under IFC 84 and MW 80 the architect or contract administrator is named in Article 3. In GC/Works/1 Edition 3 there is a division of responsibilities for dealing with contractors' claims for prolongation and disruption. Details of disruption (ie the basis of a claim) are given to the project manager, whereas assessment is clearly stated to be the function of the named quantity surveyor.

2.03   An architect or engineer, whether described as such or as contract administrator or supervising officer, has no contractual links with the contractor. He is subject to a form of appointment with the employer and this may be a standard **RIBA** or **ACE** form or a specially drafted appointment. The question inevitably arises: to what extent can the architect be genuinely impartial and administer the contract fairly? Stories are legion amongst contractors, albeit notoriously difficult to prove, of architectural practices with a small or even single client base which cannot afford to offend the paymaster.

2.04   The courts have had great difficulty in defining an architect's or engineer's obligations to employer and contractor respectively. If anything, the duty to the employer is more easily described and has caused the courts fewer problems.

2.05   In the late 19th and early 20th centuries the courts held, somewhat confusingly, that an architect or engineer held sway between the parties as an arbitrator or quasi-arbitrator (*Jackson v Barry Railway Company* (1893)). This unfortunate choice of words created the false impression that an architect's or engineer's role was somehow judicial as opposed to merely administrative. The 19th-century courts did however confirm that engineers and architects had the primary duties of honesty and, although somewhat biased because of the relationship with the employer, impartiality. In a later decision (*Hickman & Co. v Roberts and Others* (1913)) the architect delayed payment to the contractor on the specific instructions of the employer. In holding that it was improper for the employer to interfere with the certifier's discretion under the contract, the House of Lords made a number of interesting observations. In the great majority of cases an architect, although the agent of the employer, frequently had to adjudicate upon matters for which he himself was partly responsible. It was therefore imperative that architects and engineers were able to maintain a fair and judicial view of the rights of the parties. In the words of Lord Alverstone:

> 'It is therefore very important that it should be understood that when a builder or contractor puts himself in the hands of an engineer or architect as arbitrator there is a very high duty on the part of that architect or that engineer to maintain his judicial position.' (p234)

2.06   Contemporary case law has criticised as inappropriate language that ascribes a judicial or arbitral function to the architect or engineer as certifier. Repeated references by judges to the architect or engineer as arbitrator or quasi-arbitrator meant that the architect or engineer was placed in a position where he could not be sued for the consequences of his professional negligence or incompetence. It gave architects and engineers a form of judicial immunity. The result was that an employer could not recover any of his financial losses caused by the appointment of an incompetent architect or engineer. For instance, in *Chambers v Goldthorpe* (1901) a building owner unsuccessfully sued the construction professional for negligent certification which resulted in overpayment to the contractor. The court held that, when certifying, the construction professional had to act impartially towards employer and contractor. Although not an arbitrator in the strict sense of the term, an architect was, in the words of A.L. Smith MR:

> 'in the position of a person who had to exercise functions of a judicial character as between two parties, and therefore was not liable to any action for negligence in respect of what he did in the exercise of those functions.' (p 636)

This remained the position until the decision of the House of Lords in *Sutcliffe v Thackrah and Others* (1974), a case which reversed *Chambers v Goldthorpe*.

2.07   The House of Lords held in *Sutcliffe* that an architect, in certifying, was acting not as an arbitrator or quasi-arbitrator but as the agent of the employer. As such, he was liable to the employer for negligent supervision. In the particular case the architect, having overvalued building work, issued interim certificates based on that valuation, which meant that the contractor was overpaid. The employer subsequently engaged a replacement contractor to complete the building works and make good defective work. Following the original contractor's liquidation, the employer was unable to recover the overpayment from the contractor and sued the architect for negligent certification. To quote from the judgment of Lord Reid:

> '... the architect has two different types of function to perform. In many matters he is bound to act on his client's instructions, whether he agrees with them or not; but in many other matters requiring professional skill he must form and act on his own opinion.

> The building owner and the contractor make their contract on the understanding that in all such matters (eg where he has to value work, or approve it) the architect will act in a fair and unbiased manner and it must therefore be implicit in the owner's contract with the architect that he shall not only

exercise due care and skill but also reach such decisions fairly holding the balance between his client and the contractor.' (p21)

2.08   The architect's duty has of course been discussed in other modern cases. Many construction professionals are well acquainted with the decision in *London Borough of Merton v Stanley Hugh Leach Ltd* (1985). Apart from reviewing a range of other construction law issues, Vinelott J defined the role of the architect in the following terms:

'The Contract also confers on the Architect discretionary duties which he must exercise with due regard to the interests of the Contractor and the Building Owner. The Building Owner does not undertake [in respect of those discretionary duties] that the Architect will exercise his discretionary powers reasonably; he undertakes that although the Architect may be engaged or employed by him, he will leave him free to exercise his discretions fairly and without improper interference.' (p78)

2.09   What is more difficult to assess is the architect's potential liability to the contractor if the architect is incompetent in the discharge of his duties. Here the law is unfortunately in a muddle. It would seem only fair that the architect should have a duty to the contractor to exercise reasonable skill and care when issuing payment certificates (including any ascertainment of loss and expense) or granting extensions of time. There is certainly some case law to support this proposition, including favourable judicial comments in *Lubenham Fidelities and Investment Co Ltd v South Pembrokeshire District Council and Another* (1986) and *Shui On Constructions Ltd v Shui Kai Co Ltd* (1985). Most pertinent is the decision in *Michael Salliss & Co Ltd v Carlil and William F. Newman & Associates* (1987), where the Official Referee, Judge Fox-Andrews, concluded that a contractor had a right to recover damages against an unfair architect:

'If the architect unfairly promotes the building employer's interest by low certification or merely fails properly to exercise reasonable care and skill in his certification it is reasonable that the contractor should not only have the right as against the owner to have the certificate reviewed in arbitration but should also have the right to recover damages against the unfair architect.' (p78)

2.10   Following the simple and uncomplicated approach of *Michael Salliss*, the law was unfortunately thrown into confusion by the decision of the Court of Appeal in *Pacific Associates Inc and Another v Baxter and Others* (1988). The contractor was employed under an amended FIDIC form for international civil engineering works. The contractor made a 'hard materials' claim for the costs resulting from alleged errors in the borehole reports. The engineer refused to certify any additional payments. In subsequent litigation the contractor alleged that the engineer had been negligent and had failed to act impartially when certifying. The Court of Appeal decided on the facts presented to it that the contractor had established no duty of care between the engineer and him. Two arguments were crucial in reaching that conclusion. First, there was a disclaimer in the contract between the employer and the contractor. This excluded any personal liability on the part of the engineer and his staff. Even on the most superficial analysis and with no disrespect to the Court of Appeal, the ready acceptance by the Court of Appeal of the engineer's right to rely on a disclaimer in a contract to which he was not a party was a legal nonsense. Second, and of greater general importance given the prevalence of arbitration provisions in all standard form building and civil engineering contracts, the Court of Appeal concluded (without the apparent benefit of previous legal authority) that the existence of an arbitration provision in the contract between employer and contractor was effective to exclude the creation of any direct duty upon the engineer towards the contractor.

2.11   What was not discussed by the Court of Appeal, being irrelevant on the facts of the actual case, was the nature of the relationship between architect or engineer and contractor in the absence of any arbitration clause or specific disclaimer. In choosing not to discuss more fully and generally the architect's or engineer's duty of care to a contractor, the Court of Appeal left room for fresh analysis of the problem in future cases. To that extent, *Pacific Associates* may not offer the negligent certifier total protection against contractors' claims. Courts may decide to distinguish *Pacific Associates*, if necessary, as having been decided on its own particular facts. This device is used by lawyers to explain away problematic decisions of the courts which seem to defy an ordinary understanding of the law. Leaving to one side the slightly unusual contract form in *Pacific Associates*, which included a specific disclaimer about the certifier's duty to the contractor, the principle established does appear to be otherwise relevant to the architect's position under contracts of the JCT family.

2.12 The return to a more realistic approach is found in *Davy Offshore Ltd v Emerald Field Contracting Ltd* (1991). In the words of the Official Referee, Judge Thayne Forbes:

> 'In my judgment, it is clear that the obligation to act fairly is concerned with those duties of the architect/engineer which require him to use his professional judgment in holding the balance between his client and the contractor. Such duties are those where the architect/engineer is obliged to make a decision or form an opinion which affect the rights of the parties to the contract, for example, valuations of work, ascertaining direct loss and expense, granting extensions of time, etc. When making such decisions pursuant to his duties under the contract, the architect/engineer is obliged to act fairly'. (p146)

2.13 In law, for the architect or engineer to be liable to the contractor (with whom ordinarily he has no contract) the principles establishing the legal doctrine of tort must be satisfied. In essence, the law of tort recognises that party A may, if he is negligent in his actions, cause loss or physical harm to party B for which party A should compensate party B. To avoid open-ended and indiscriminate liability, the courts have over the years set parameters for the recovery of loss. For there to be liability in tort the law requires:

- a sufficiently close relationship between party A and party B;
- loss or damage of a type which is foreseeable as likely to flow from party A's original negligent actions; and
- the loss or damage not to be too remote from party A's original negligent actions, ie the loss or damage was not caused by some intervening event or, subject to certain exceptions, the result of circumstances special to party B.

2.14 The law clearly recognises that party A is liable to be sued by party B for the consequences of the former's negligence which causes physical harm to party B. A simple example would be the negligent car driver who, in knocking down a pedestrian, causes the latter personal injuries. When the scenario changes to one where the harm caused to party B by party A is pure financial loss, the courts have struggled for consistency and a coherent response. This type of claim is often referred to as 'pure economic loss' and would include the case of the contractor and the negligent certifier. In recent years courts have taken a restrictive view of those financial losses that are recoverable. This may be a major reason why *Pacific Associates* could appear to have reached a seemingly illogical conclusion. The decision may simply have coincided with a period when the courts were tending to vacillate in their approach to economic loss claims. *Pacific Associates* may erroneously have been caught up in the climate created by the cases of negligently constructed buildings which neither caused physical harm nor produced a threat of physical harm.

2.15   In *Murphy v Brentwood District Council* (1991) the House of Lords completed the task commenced by a differently constituted House of Lords in *D. & F. Estates Ltd and Others v Church Commissioners for England and Others* (1989). The *Murphy* case, where the claim was brought against the local authority in respect of negligent inspection of defectively designed foundations to a domestic dwelling house, established that a plaintiff under English law could not recover the cost of repairing a defective item where damage did not extend beyond the item itself. Interestingly, in Canada the Supreme Court decided by a 4:3 majority in *Norsk Steamship Company Ltd v Canadian National Railway Co* (1992) not to follow *Murphy*.

2.16   The cases of so-called negligent mis-statement, which must include the negligent certifier and contractor situation, represent the major exception to the *Murphy* principle. 'Negligent mis-statement' is a relatively recent notion and finds its roots in the decision of the House of Lords in *Hedley Byrne and Co Ltd v Heller and Partners Ltd* (1964), where the plaintiff had suffered financial losses because of negligent financial advice given to him by the defendant. The House of Lords was satisfied that the defendant was aware that his advice would be relied upon and it was foreseeable that, if the advice was bad, the plaintiff would suffer loss. On the facts of the particular case the defendant was saved from the consequences of his own negligence because he had qualified his advice with a disclaimer of responsibility. Since *Hedley Byrne* the courts have consistently held that a plaintiff is entitled to recover his financial losses in circumstances where he relied on the oral or written advice or other written statement of a party, and the party knew that the advice or written statement in question would be relied upon.

2.17   The most recent important restatement of the *Hedley Byrne* principle was by the House of Lords in *Caparo Industries Plc v Dickman and Others* (1990). Touche Ross, the accountants, were auditors of Fidelity, a public company. Caparo made a successful bid for Fidelity in reliance, it alleged, on Fidelity's audited accounts. Caparo commenced proceedings against Touche Ross alleging negligence in certifying the accounts. The argument advanced was that Touche Ross owed a duty of care to investors and potential investors in respect of the audit. The House of Lords took the opportunity to re-emphasise that at the heart of all negligent mis-statement cases was the need for reliance by party A on party B. It was always necessary to prove that a defendant knew that his statement would be communicated to the plaintiff, either as an individual or as a member of an identifiable class, for a specific purpose and that the plaintiff was very likely to rely upon it.

2.18   Without recourse to the intellectual sleight of accepting that *Pacific Associates* was decided upon its own particular facts, it is extremely difficult to reconcile the Court of Appeal's decision with that of a superior court, the House of Lords, in the slightly later case of *Caparo*. The retreat from *Pacific Associates* is clearly seen in the unreported Australian case, *R.W. Miller and Co Pty Ltd v Krupp (Australia) Pty Ltd* (1992). Although the plaintiff's claim in negligence was dismissed in accordance with the *Pacific Associates* principle, the judge concluded that *Pacific Associates* clearly 'turned on the particular circumstances' in which the 'contractual framework' had applied.

3   Claims for breach of contract

3.01   Although most contractors claim additional monies (often referred to in the JCT terminology, 'loss and expense') for delay and disruption caused by late information, instructions, failure to give possession of the site, etc under the contract (eg under Clause 26 of JCT 80, Clauses 46 and 47 of GC/Works/1 Edition 3, Clauses 4·11–4·12 of IFC 84), they also have a concurrent right at common law to claim damages for breach of contract. This is made clear by the contractual provisions. For instance, Clause 26·6 of JCT 80 indicates that a contractor's right to make a contractual claim under Clause 26 is additional to and not a replacement for rights at common law:

> 'The provisions of Clause 26 are without prejudice to any other rights and remedies which the Contractor may possess.'

The contractor's right to bring a common law damages claim was litigated in the context of JCT 63 in *London Borough of Merton v Stanley Hugh Leach Ltd* (1985). In that case, Vinelott J said:

> '[The contractor] may prefer to wait until completion of the work and join the claim for damages for breach of the obligation to provide instructions, drawings and the like in good time with other claims for damages for breach of obligations under the contract.' (p108)

Unless a contractor has failed to comply with particular contract provisions which are conditions precedent to the making of claims under the contract's loss and expense clauses (eg the service of written notices), contractual claims are usually more advantageous to him than claims at common law for damages. Claims under the contract are certified by the architect with the monies ascertained being added to interim certificates. This obviously assists the contractor's cash flow. Further, certain of the events which allow the operation of the loss and expense provisions are not themselves breaches of contract either at common law or under the contract.

3.02   A provision similar to Clause 26·6 of JCT 80 is found in Clause 4·11 of IFC 84 but not in MW 80, which is silent generally on the question of contractual claims for loss and expense. Although MW

80 can be amended to include a loss and expense provision of the JCT 80 or IFC 84 type, ordinarily the contractor will be left to argue that a failure to comply with specific terms of the contract or the consequences of complying with particular clauses can give rise to additional monies. Such clauses would include:

- Failure to issue further necessary information (Clause 1·2)
- Failure to allow commencement on the due date (Clause 2·1)
- Instructions (Clause 3·5)

Alternatively, like a JCT 80 or IFC 84 contractor, an MW 80 contractor can on occasions allege breach of the implied terms as the basis of his claim. Implied terms are more fully discussed in paragraphs 3.09–20 inclusive.

3.03   The fact that contractors seemingly have a second bite at the cherry in addition to contractual claims poses a number of questions. These include:

- What is the definition of common law?
- Which terms of the contract expose the employer to potential claims from the contractor for additional monies?
- Does the contract include all relevant terms for common law damages claims?

Common law

3.04   Over the centuries English law developed in two distinct ways with the growth of common law and equity in different courts, and this duality makes any attempt at a definition difficult. In general the common law can be taken to be the law of England and Wales as it developed in the case law decisions of the courts. Alongside it the doctrine of equity evolved, with its ability to look outside the strict contractual rights and obligations of the parties. Amongst other applications it can in certain circumstances allow the rectification or rescission of contracts or the granting of injunctions. Equity came to provide a safety net to respond to those situations where the strict application of the common law in its full vigour would not achieve justice between the parties.

3.05   The main feature of the common law is that ordinarily a decision of a superior court will bind all inferior courts. For this reason all

High Court and County Court judges must follow decisions of the Court of Appeal, while decisions of the House of Lords will bind all other judges, including those of the Court of Appeal. Until recent years even the House of Lords was bound to follow its own previous decisions, although this practice has now fallen into disuse. A notable modern example was the decision in *Murphy v Brentwood District Council* (1990), where the House of Lords chose to reverse the earlier decision in *Anns and Others v Merton London Borough Council* (1978).

3.06   Common law continues to develop. Decisions of High Court judges are often reversed by the Court of Appeal and those of the Court of Appeal by the House of Lords. At times particular judges resort to distinguishing troublesome and apparently conflicting decisions of earlier judges, even to the extent of concluding that an unhelpful judgment in an earlier case was the result of facts peculiar to the specific case. Increasingly, important inroads are made into the common law by Parliament, a tendency that will accelerate following developments in European law with its desire to cut across national differences and harmonise the approach in member states of the European Union to particular issues.

3.07   At any time Parliament can modify the common law by means of statutory law, either in the form of an Act of Parliament or a statutory instrument. Further, Directives and other legislation from the European Union, which are already significant for English lawyers, are likely to have increasing effect on the English common law in the years to come. One example of legislative control over the common law is the modification by statute of the common law rules on exclusion and limitation of liability clauses. Domestic legislation in the form of the Unfair Contract Terms Act 1977 already restricts, more than does the common law, a party's right in some situations to rely on an exclusion or limitation of liability clause to protect itself from the consequences of its own breaches of contract. This Act will itself now be subject to further modification by an EC Directive on Unfair Contract Terms in Consumer Contracts 93/13/EEC, which is due to be adopted in member countries by 31 December 1994.

3.08   Many, if not all, of the circumstances which permit a contractor to recover additional monies under Clause 26 of JCT 80 and analogous contract provisions are also breaches of contract at common law. Non-compliance with, amongst others, the following clauses would be breach of express terms of JCT 80:

- Discrepancy in or divergence between documents as defined (Clause 2·3).
- Immediate provision by the Architect on execution of the Contract of a set or sets of the Contract Documents, Drawings, unpriced Bills of Quantities (if not already provided) (Clause 5·2).
- Further information as and when reasonably required by the Contractor 'either to explain and amplify the Contract Drawings or to enable the Contractor to carry out and complete the Works in accordance with the Conditions' (Clause 5·4).
- On the Date of Possession possession of the site shall be given to the Contractor (Clause 23·1·1).

3.09   In addition to the express terms of a contract (ie those set out on the face of any written agreement evidencing the contract or agreed by the parties to an oral contract), what comes as a surprise to many non-lawyers is that the common law allows additional clauses to be read into any contract, including a written one. Even if a contract is set out at great length, such as JCT 80, the common law allows additional terms to be construed as part of the contract. Clause 2·1 of JCT 80 which states:

> 'The Contractor shall upon and subject to the Conditions carry out and complete the Works shown upon the Contract Drawings ...'

is not effective to prevent the implication, as necessary, of further contract terms, and the position is similar under Clause 1·1 of IFC 84 and 1·1 of MW 80. Contract conditions which are not expressly referred to by the parties at the date the contract is formed but which nevertheless bind the parties, are called implied terms.

Implied terms

3.10   Terms may be implied into contracts for the following reasons:

- by statute;
- to give the contract 'business efficacy';
- on the 'officious bystander' test;
- through custom and practice of the trade;

•   because of previous dealings between the parties during which they have repeatedly traded on the same terms.

3.11   Examples of terms implied by statute include the following. Goods supplied will be of merchantable quality and, subject to certain qualifications, fit for their purpose (Sale of Goods Act 1979). The Sale and Supply of Goods Bill which is before Parliament at the date of writing will substitute the concept of 'satisfactory quality' for 'merchantable quality'. Similarly, those who provide professional services should be reasonably competent and use reasonable skill and care (Supply of Goods and Services Act 1982).

3.12   By far the most important ways of introducing additional obligations, ie implied terms, into construction contracts are on the 'business efficacy' or 'officious bystander' tests. These presuppose that there are certain terms which are so self-evidently required to make the parties' contract work that they must be read into the contract in order to make it commercially effective. This will happen even if the parties failed to mention the particular terms at the time they made their contract. A famous example was *The Moorcock* (1889). The defendants were wharfingers who had agreed to allow the plaintiff to unload his vessel at their jetty. The jetty extended into the Thames and, as both parties realised, the vessel had to ground at low water. When the tide ebbed, the vessel settled on a hard ridge and was damaged. The plaintiff sued for the resultant damage with the Court of Appeal holding that the defendants had, as far as was reasonable, warranted that the river bottom was not in such a condition as to endanger the vessel.

3.13   What are significant for present purposes are the comments of the judges over the years on the 'business efficacy' and 'officious bystander' tests. Two illustrative examples are *Reigate v Union Manufacturing Co (Ramsbottom) Ltd and Elton Cop Dyeing Co Ltd* (1918) and *Shirlaw v Southern Foundries (1926) Ltd* (1939). In *Reigate*, Scrutton LJ said:

> 'A term can only be implied if it is necessary in the business sense to give efficacy to the contract, that is, if it is such a term that it can confidently be said that if at the time the contract was being negotiated someone had said to the parties: 'What will happen in such a case' they would both have replied: "Of course so and so will happen; we did not trouble to say that; it is too clear."' (p605)

In *Shirlaw*, MacKinnon LJ said:

> 'Prima facie that which in any contract is left to be implied and need not be expressed is something so obvious that it goes without saying; so that, if while the parties were making their bargain an officious bystander were to suggest some express provision for it in their agreement, they would testily suppress him with a common, "Oh, of course!"' (p227)

3.14   What the courts will never do is imply terms into contracts merely to extricate a party from the consequences of a badly drafted document. This point was neatly emphasised by the House of Lords in *Trollope & Colls Ltd v North-West Metropolitan Regional Hospital Board* (1973). Building works were to be carried out in three phases with Phase III due to start at a date fixed by reference to the completion date of Phase I. There was a stated date for completion of Phase III. Substantial delays to Phase I reduced the time available to complete Phase III. The contractor argued, in vain, that the period for completion of Phase III should be extended to take account of the overrun on Phase I. Lord Pearson concluded:

> 'The Court does not make a contract for the parties. The Court will not even improve the contract which the parties have made for themselves, however desirable the improvement might be ... If the express terms are perfectly clear and free from ambiguity, there is no choice to be made between different possible meanings; the clear terms must be applied even if the Court thinks some other terms would have been more suitable. An unexpressed term can be implied if and only if the Court finds that the parties must have intended that term to form part of their contract; ... it must have been a term that went without saying, a term necessary to give business efficacy to the contract, a term which, though tacit, formed part of the contract which the parties made for themselves.' (p70)

3.15   The implication of further terms into construction contracts is common, although an implied term can never be added where the contract already contains an express term in regard to a particular obligation. The most obvious example of an implied term in a construction contract is the composite duty on an employer to co-operate with a contractor in the carrying out of building works.

This obligation was stressed by Viscount Simon LC in *Luxor (Eastbourne) Ltd and Others v Cooper* (1941):

> 'Generally speaking, where B is employed by A to do a piece of work which requires A's co-operation ... it is implied that the necessary co-operation will be forthcoming.' (p118)

3.16   Of all the cases which discuss the implication of terms into building contracts, perhaps the two most important decisions for construction professionals to know are *Merton v Leach* (1985) and *Davy Offshore Ltd v Emerald Field Contracting Ltd* (1991). Alongside these may now have to be considered *J & J Fee Ltd v The Express Lift Co Ltd* (1993).

3.17   The first case concerned a JCT 63 contract (July 1971 Revision) for the construction of 287 new dwellings. The contract price was £2,265,000 with completion within 33 months of the date of possession. In considering a myriad of complex issues the judge held that the following implied terms were to be read as part of JCT 63 in addition to the express conditions:

•   Merton would not hinder or prevent Leach from carrying out their obligations in accordance with the terms of the contract or in their execution of work in a regular and orderly manner, eg by the provision of late drawings or information.
•   The implied obligation on the employer to provide information timeously extended to the architect. The employer was liable for any delays by the architect in the provision of information to the contractor.
•   The architect would provide the contractor with the full, correct and co-ordinated information concerning the works.
•   The architect was to administer the contract in an efficient and proper manner.

3.18   The second case concerned a detailed 'design and construct' contract for the provision of a floating production and storage facility in a North Sea oil field. The contractor tried to imply additional terms into an already lengthy contract. The judge started by referring to a 'check list' of conditions which need to be satisfied before additional terms can be implied into a detailed written contract. The requirements necessary, which may overlap, were identified by the Privy Council in an earlier Australian case, *B.P. Refinery (Westernport) Pty Ltd v Shire of Hastings* (1978).

- The term must be reasonable and equitable.
- It must be necessary to give business efficacy to the contract. No term can be implied if the contract is effective without it.
- It must be so obvious that 'it goes without saying'.
- It must be capable of clear expression.
- It must not contradict any express term of the contract.

3.19   On the particular facts of *Davy Offshore*, the contractor alleged that four further terms should be implied into the contract. These were:

- The employer was not to hinder or prevent the contractor carrying out the works.
- The employer would carry out his contractual obligations within a reasonable time so as not to impede the contractor.
- The employer would operate the variations clause 'fairly'.
- The employer would name a replacement sub-contractor to replace, as necessary, an original 'named', though not nominated, sub-contractor.

3.20   The responses of the Court were as follows:

- A term of 'non-impedance' is to be implied into a contract in appropriate circumstances. This proposition is well supported by a number of case law decisions. These include *Merton v Leach* (1985), *Perini Corporation v Commonwealth of Australia* (1969), and *Barque Cuilpué Ltd v Brown* (1904). However, on the facts of *Davy Offshore* such a further term was unnecessary. By Clause 33·1 of the contract 'the employer was not [to] delay or obstruct the contractor in the performance of the work'. It was a well established principle of contract law that the courts would not imply a term where there was already an express term.

- When the contract requires the employer to do something and 'where the contract does not specify within what time action should be taken', there is an implied term which obliges the employer to act within a reasonable time necessary to facilitate the contractor. The common law has a well developed doctrine of co-operation, albeit limited to what is in all the circumstances reasonable (*Mona Oil Equipment & Supply Co Ltd v Rhodesia Railways Ltd* (1949); *Merton v Leach* (1985)).

- In dealing with variations there is an obligation on the

employer, engineer or architect to act fairly in the discharge of any duties and to use professional skill and judgment in making decisions. This was a well established and known principle (*Holland Hannen & Cubitts (Northern) Ltd v Welsh Health Technical Services Organisation and Others* (1981)). On the particular facts of *Davy Offshore*, which had express provisions for variations, the implied term was not to be included.

• Again, on the particular facts of *Davy Offshore*, the judge did not need to consider the question of choosing a new sub-contractor. The principle in *T.A. Bickerton & Son Ltd v North West Metropolitan Regional Hospital Board* (1970) did not apply. There was an express term in the contract that 'the contractor [is] entitled to complete the work himself or engage another sub-contractor to complete it'.

3.21   In *J & J Fee Ltd* the plaintiff was main contractor for the construction of an eight-storey office block on the Isle of Dogs, London. The main contract was in the standard form JCT 81 With Contractor's Design. Fee entered into a sub-contract with the defendant for the manufacture, delivery and installation of two passenger lifts. Fee claimed damages against the sub-contractor for late completion. Both plaintiff and defendant were in agreement that although no standard form of sub-contract had ever been signed, the DOM/2 Conditions of Sub-contract applied. Although there were four issues to be considered by the judge, the important one related to whether or not there were implied terms in the sub-contract of the type alleged by the defendant. During the trial, the parties agreed that there were implied terms as follows:

> 'The plaintiff by itself its servants agents or sub-contractors would:
>
> (a) not hinder or prevent the defendant from carrying out its obligations under the terms of the sub-contract;
> (b) take all steps reasonably necessary to enable the defendant to discharge its obligations under the terms of the sub-contract.'

The one remaining implied term that the defendant wished to establish, and which was the source of some contention, was:

'(c) *provide the defendant with* [full] *correct* [and

comprehensive] *information concerning the works* in such a manner and at such times as was reasonably necessary for the defendant to have in order for it to fulfil its obligations under the sub-contract.'

It was agreed between the respective Counsel that the words in square brackets should be omitted from the alleged implied term and that the words in italics should be included as part of the term to be implied by the court. The argument was limited to those words that were neither in square brackets nor italics. The judge held that it was an implied term that the plaintiff provide the defendant with correct information concerning the works in such manner and at such times as was reasonably necessary for the defendant to have it in order for it to fulfil its obligations under the sub-contract. In the words of the Official Referee, Judge Bowsher:

'There is nothing in this contract, DOM/2, which puts on the contractor an express duty to provide necessary information. For that reason it is agreed by the parties that a term should be implied into the contract that information should be supplied. The contract cannot be made to work unless the information is supplied: it is essential. Moreover, there is no point in supplying that information unless it is supplied in such a manner and at such times as is reasonably necessary for Express to have it in order for Express to fulfil their obligations under the sub-contract. It is necessary and it is reasonable that the whole of the implied term for which Express contends should be implied into the contract. It is not necessary or reasonable that it should be implied that Express should only be given essential information if they ask for it in writing. I see no inconsistency between such an implied term and the express terms of DOM/2.' (p841)

3.22 A contractor who alleges the employer is in breach of contract, whether as a result of the latter's failure to comply with the express terms or with the implied ones in the contract, must establish three things. First, he must show that he has suffered loss caused by the employer's breach of contract; second, he must demonstrate that the loss he has suffered is sufficiently linked to the employer's breach or breaches of contract so as to satisfy the test for the recovery of damages first set down in *Hadley v Baxendale* (1854). (The issue of causation is considered in

paragraphs 3.23–25, and that of the *Hadley v Baxendale* test in
3.29–31.) Third, his loss must be an actual financial one and not
merely a notional loss. In summation, as in all civil claims, the
contractor must prove his case 'on the balance of probabilities'.

Causation

3.23   A leading legal textbook described the issue of causation in this
way:

> 'Causation is a knotty problem, and the reports are full of
> expressions such as direct cause, proximate cause, effective
> cause, breaking the chain of causation, supervening cause.
> These familiar terms are in many ways more of a hindrance
> than a help because their very familiarity has blunted any
> precision of meaning they may have once had.' (*McGregor on
> Damages*, Sweet & Maxwell, 15th Ed. 1988, para. 134)

3.24   On construction contracts facts frequently become confused.
Although the employer may have contributed significantly to a
contractor's delay, it may also be the case that the contractor has
some responsibility for his own delay. Different courts have
reached different and often contradictory conclusions on how to
deal with this situation. On balance, it would appear that a
contractor will succeed if he establishes that the cause for which
the employer is liable was the effective/dominant cause of his loss.
Surprisingly, there are no construction law cases specifically on the
point. The issue, which is also relevant to the question of
concurrent delays and extensions of time, has arisen in a number
of marine insurance cases. In *Yorkshire Dale Steamship Company
Ltd v Minister of War Transport* (1942), a ship had been stranded
near the Outer Hebrides. This was partly because the navigator
had chosen a route to avoid enemy submarines and partly because
there was an unusual tidal set which had taken the vessel too close
to rocks. Viscount Simon LC concluded that:

> 'One has to ask oneself what was the effective and
> predominant cause of the accident that happened, whatever
> the nature of that accident may be.' (p698)

3.25   Although the effective or dominant cause approach is generally
adopted, it has at times been said that if part of the damage is due

to a breach of contract by the plaintiff, he must show how much of the damage is caused otherwise than by his own breach of contract. If he fails to achieve this any recovery of damages is only nominal. This approach was adopted in *Government of Ceylon v Chandris* (1965). In one construction law case, *H. Fairweather & Co Ltd v London Borough of Wandsworth* (1987), the judge considered *obiter* the question of concurrent delays in the context of extensions of time. It was his opinion that the dominant cause test was incorrect. However, the Court of Appeal confirmed in *Galoo Ltd and Others v Bright Grahame Murray* (1994) that the dominant or effective cause approach is correct rather than the 'but for' test which is also sometimes used.

3.26 Although certain claims consultants appear in their presentation of claims to ignore the questions of causation and proof, mere assertion of a contractual right is insufficient. The contractor must always demonstrate by the use of oral or documentary evidence that his loss was as a consequence of the employer's breach and was an actual one. It is insufficient for it to be based on a theoretical extrapolation. In *C & P Haulage v Middleton* (1983), Ackner LJ stated:

> 'It is not the function of the Courts where there is a breach of contract knowingly ... to put the plaintiff in a better financial position than if the contract had been properly performed.' (p1467)

That said, the editors of *Keating on Building Contracts* (Sweet & Maxwell, 5th Ed. 1991, p209) see certain benefits in a contractor seeking damages at common law rather than relying on a contractual remedy. Matters of doubt may be resolved in the contractor's favour where the quality of the proof advanced is imperfect:

> 'Where the [Contractor's] claim is for breach of contract the court is the more likely to resolve matters of doubt in the contractor's favour and, even where the evidence of loss is very unsatisfactory, if satisfied that there was substantial loss, will make some award.'

3.27 The effect of the Law Reform (Contributory Negligence) Act 1945 on claims in contract was considered in *Barclays Bank Plc v Fairclough Building Ltd* (1994). Fairclough was carrying out work on storage buildings of the bank in Manchester. The roofs of the buildings were of corrugated asbestos sheeting and were not watertight. This resulted in asbestos slurry entering and scattering throughout the buildings. The dried residue polluted the buildings which had to be taken out of use and cleaned up. The bank argued the contractor had not acted with reasonable skill and care and that it was in breach of the terms of the contract by failing to comply with the asbestos regulations. Fairclough tried to rely on the 1945 Act to reduce its financial liability. Although the case could have been decided entirely in tort, the fact that Fairclough was also in breach of contract did not, in the trial judge's opinion, prevent the 1945 Act applying to the claim in contract. On appeal, it was held in the Court of Appeal that a defendant to a claim for breach of contract could not rely in his defence on a plea that the plaintiff had been contributorily negligent. The Law Reform (Contributory Negligence) Act 1945 only applied to a breach of the duty of care in tort (negligence).

3.28   Although the case was not concerned with prolongation and disruption costs, in *George Fisher (GB) Limited v Multiconstruction Ltd and Dexion Ltd* (1992), Judge Hicks, sitting as an Official Referee, made an award of damages in the plaintiff's favour on less than perfect evidence. He said:

> 'I bear in mind that the onus of proving damages is on the plaintiff, but where they have produced some evidence of such damage I must make the best assessment of the amount that I can on the evidence available. It would, of course, seriously discount, if not negate, the level of any award if the proper inference from failure to call customers were that the plaintiff expected that they would have given evidence adverse to the plaintiff's case ...' (p797)

The Hadley v Baxendale test

3.29   In order for damages to be recoverable they must not be too remote from the original breach of contract. This principle, originally laid down in *Hadley v Baxendale*, has been applied and explained on many subsequent occasions. Perhaps the two most important modern decisions are those in *Victoria Laundry (Windsor) Ltd v Newman Industries Ltd* (1949) and *Koufos v C. Czarnikow Ltd (The Heron II)* (1969), although the application of the *Hadley v Baxendale* principle was considered afresh by the House of Lords (Scotland) in *Balfour Beatty Construction (Scotland) Ltd v Scottish Power Plc* (1994). To begin with *Hadley v Baxendale*, the facts were relatively simple. The plaintiff's mill was brought to a standstill when the only crankshaft broke. The defendant carrier failed to deliver the broken shaft to the manufacturer at the promised time. The plaintiff sued for the profits he would have made had the mill started working again without the delay. The claim was rejected because it was unreasonable to fix the defendant with the knowledge that an unreasonable delay in the delivery of the broken shaft to the manufacturer would leave the plaintiff's mill at a standstill. In an often repeated judgment by Alderson B the court held:

> 'Where two parties have made a contract which one of them has broken, the damages which the other party ought to receive in respect of such breach of contract should be such as may fairly and reasonably be considered either as arising naturally, ie according to the usual course of things, from such breach of contract itself, or such as may reasonably be supposed to have been in the contemplation of both parties at the time they made the contract, as the probable result of the breach of it.' (p341)

3.30   The two propositions put forward in *Hadley v Baxendale* are often referred to as the first and second rules. The first rule encompasses those losses that flow naturally from the defendant's breach of contract, a concept which itself has led to considerable litigation. The second applies to those losses that are particular to the plaintiff and the likelihood of which occurring on a future breach of contract was either known to or could reasonably have been anticipated by the parties at the date the contract was made. Therefore, if special circumstances which affect the plaintiff are unknown to the defendant at the date the contract is made, the contract breaker can only be supposed to have had in his contemplation the general level of damages which would flow from his breach of contract, ie those within the so-called first rule. In *Victoria Laundry* the plaintiff could not recover from the defendant damages for the loss of a particularly lucrative contract. The loss fell outside both the rules in *Hadley v Baxendale*. The facts were as follows. The plaintiff company decided to extend its laundry and dyeing business. In order to obtain some especially

lucrative dyeing contracts a large boiler was required. The
defendant engineering company failed to deliver the necessary
boiler by the agreed date. Although it was foreseeable to the
defendant that the plaintiff would suffer some loss of profit as a
result of the late commissioning of the boiler and could therefore
recover a general conjectural sum for 'normal' loss of use, the
additional losses were non-recoverable.

3.31   The test for the recoverability of financial loss was stated slightly
differently in *The Heron II*. It was not a question whether the
damage should have been foreseen by the defendant but whether
the probability of its occurrence should have been within the
reasonable contemplation of both parties at the time the contract
was made, having regard to their knowledge at the time. In the
words of Lord Upjohn:

> 'In contract the parties have only to consider the consequences
> of a breach to the other; it is fair that the assessment of
> damages should depend on their assumed common knowledge
> and contemplation and not on a foreseeable but most unlikely
> consequence.' (p442)

3.32   In *Balfour Beatty Construction*, Balfour Beatty was the main
contractor for the construction of the roadway and associated
structures of a section of the Edinburgh by-pass. As part of the
works a concrete batching plant was installed a few miles away
and an agreement made with the South of Scotland Electricity
Board for the provision of a temporary supply of electricity.
During the construction of a concrete aquaduct, the concrete
plant ceased to operate due to the rupturing of fuses provided by
the Board in the supply system. As a result of the failure, the
aquaduct could no longer be completed to the standard required
and what had been constructed had to be demolished and
subsequently re-built. Balfour Beatty sought to recover from the
Board, as damages, the cost of demolition and reconstruction.
Balfour Beatty's claim was rejected because, in the words of
Lord Jauncey:

> 'The defenders could certainly contemplate that if the supply
> failed the plant would not operate and that if it was operating
> at the time the manufacture of concrete would be interrupted.
> What they did not know was the necessity of preserving a
> continuous pour for the purposes of the particular operation ...

> It may be that the technique of a continuous pour for certain
> concrete structures may be a regular part of industrial
> practice, and it may be that the fact that if concrete is poured
> into position it will harden is within common knowledge, but
> the fact that an interruption of the pour could lead to a
> condemnation of the whole operation seems to me to be
> beyond the defenders' reasonable contemplation.'

In accordance with the time-honoured test, the Board 'should only
be taken to have anticipated the kind of loss arising naturally in
the ordinary course of things from the breach of contract'. As a
matter of general knowledge the Board would have appreciated
that concrete poured would ultimately harden. But, that said, the
Board had no reason to be aware of the importance of the time
involved in the hardening process nor of the consequences of
adding freshly poured concrete to that which had already
hardened. In applying the first rule in *Hadley v Baxendale*,
although business parties must be taken to understand the
ordinary practices and exigencies of the other's trade:

> '... it had always to be a question of circumstances what one
> contracting party is presumed to know about the business
> activities of the other. No doubt the simpler the activity of the
> one, the more readily could it be inferred that the other would
> have reasonable knowledge thereof.'

As far as a contractor's common law claims are concerned, the
main question to consider is whether the sums recoverable are
somewhat more limited than those ascertained under the
contractual claims provisions in standard form contracts, eg
Clause 26 and Clauses 4·11–12 of IFC 84, etc. For instance,
although it is now well established that a contractor's financing
charges and head office overheads are intrinsic elements of his
claim under JCT contracts, are they recoverable as part of a
common law damages claim? Supposing that the contractor is
clearly entitled to recover his on-site establishment costs resulting
from delay together with the immediate costs caused by disrupted
working, are profits in excess of 'normal' profits and financing
charges special circumstances of the contractor outside the
employer's contemplation at the date the contract was made?

Heads of claim

3.33   Essentially any contractor's claim for additional monies for delay
        and disruption will fall within one or more of the following heads:

- Increased preliminaries
- Overheads
- Loss of profit
- Loss of productivity or uneconomic working
- Fluctuations
- Financing charges

3.34   The most common method of calculating increased preliminaries is
        to take the amounts in the Bills of Quantities and to pro rata them
        over the period of delay. This ignores the fact that common law
        damages claims must be calculated on an actual expenditure basis.
        Again, contractors tend to favour a formula approach of the
        Hudson or Emden type in the calculation of overheads and loss of
        profit. However, the Quantity Surveyors Practice Pamphlet No. 7,
        Contractor's Direct Loss and/or Expense, advises that overhead
        costs and loss of profit must be specifically calculated and proved.
        This reflects the position at common law, even if the loss and
        expense provisions in the standard form contracts are sometimes
        less rigid in their day to day operation. At common law a
        contractor is entitled to reimbursement of loss of profit if he can
        prove that he was prevented from earning profit elsewhere as a
        result of one or more breaches of contract by the employer. As a
        result of the second rule in *Hadley v Baxendale*, the contractor
        cannot recover an exceptionally high profit unless there were
        particular factors about the contract which were known to the
        employer at the date the contract was made. This accords with the
        decision in *Victoria Laundry*. In general, the loss of head office
        overheads and profit is difficult to show. Recovery is based on the
        assumption that when a contract is delayed, the contribution made
        by that particular contract to the contractor's overheads and profit
        is diminished by reason of the contractor's resources being tied up
        for longer than anticipated and not being available for deployment
        elsewhere. In theory at least it is the contractor's obligation in
        establishing the loss to show that other contracts have been lost in
        consequence. It may however be sufficient for the contractor to
        rely on a drop in turnover and a refusal to tender for other
        contracts. Frequently contractors also have great difficulties in
        establishing their disruption costs. Given that the courts seek to

recompense a party for his actual losses, theoretical formulations are to be avoided, if at all possible. Further, even the most apparently sophisticated calculations can often be shown to be fallacious, as occurred in *McAlpine Humberoak Ltd v McDermott International Inc* (1992). Any analysis must therefore be carried out on the basis of a comparison of actual labour and plant costs as against anticipated ones, giving due credit for matters that were the exclusive responsibility of the contractor. Claims for fluctuations must also be proved on an actual expenditure basis.

3.35 Contractors often seek reimbursement of the interest charges they may incur as a consequence of borrowing money because of the employer's breach or breaches of contract. Alternatively, at times a contractor will claim the interest that he was prevented from earning on his own capital as a result of having to finance the consequences of the employer's breach or breaches of contract. Although *F.G. Minter Ltd v Welsh Health Technical Services Organisation* (1980) and *Rees & Kirby Ltd v Swansea City Council* (1985) have clearly established that the contractor's financing charges are a constituent element of direct loss and/or expense and seemed to suggest common law damages and loss and expense are one and the same under JCT 80, it is quite difficult to establish a right to recover interest at common law. An old case, *The London, Chatham and Dover Railway Company v The South Eastern Railway Company* (1893), decided that there is no general right to interest on the late payment of a debt. This principle has been re-affirmed on many occasions, although there are now three major exceptions to the general rule.

3.36 First, there are particular statutes which empower a court or an arbitrator to award interest. Under s35A of the Supreme Court Act 1981, s69 of the County Courts Act 1984 and s19A of the Arbitration Act 1950, a judge or arbitrator can award interest as part of a judgment or award. The court's power to award interest from the date of judgment until the date of payment originated in the Judgment Act 1839. It was not until the enactment of s3(1) of the Law Reform (Miscellaneous Provisions) Act 1934 that the High Court was empowered to award interest between the date when 'the cause of action' accrued and the date of judgment. This provision did not apply to the County Court. The judge's power now includes the right to award interest on a debt in respect of which proceedings were commenced and which the debtor paid off prior to judgment being given. This latter power was provided to judges by the Administration of Justice Act 1982, which modified the Supreme Court Act 1981, and was reflected in the decision of the House of Lords in *President of India v La Pintada Compañía Navegación SA* (1985).

3.37 Second, certain contracts, such as the ICE Conditions of Contract 5th Edition (Clause 60(6)) and the ICE Conditions of Contract 6th Edition (Clause 60(7)), allow for the payment of interest to the contractor 'in the event of failure by the Engineer to certify or the Employer to make payment in accordance with ...' The imprecise wording has created problems. Does the contractor require a specific default or failure to apply the contract conditions correctly by the engineer, or merely a subsequent increase to amounts previously certified? *Secretary of State for Transport v Birse Farr Joint Venture* (1993) and *Royal Borough of Kingston Upon Thames v Amec Civil Engineering Ltd* (1993) appear to suggest that the first proposition is correct. The decision in *Morgan Grenfell (Local Authority Finance) Ltd v Sunderland Borough Council and Seven Seas Dredging Ltd* (1990), (where two earlier and apposite Scottish decisions were not considered) to the effect that simply to increase the previous certified value is sufficient to trigger the right to contractual interest, now appears unlikely to be followed. Provided the engineer has not demonstrably misapplied the contractual provisions or otherwise been in breach of his professional obligations, revisions to amounts certified under the contract are not to be treated as an unusual occurrence.

3.38 Although the main civil engineering contract, ICE 6th Edition, allows interest on late certification, the position is somewhat different under the JCT-type contracts in that there is no provision for contractual interest. Instead, it is necessary to look to the common law to establish whether or not a contractor might have a remedy against the employer for financing charges of the type allowed in *Minter* or for financial loss caused to him by an architect's failure either to certify valuations promptly or ascertain loss and expense in the appropriate amount at the earliest opportunity. Although not free from doubt, it is also arguable that a contractor might be entitled to claim such losses as special damages under the second rule in *Hadley v Baxendale* in both these situations. This provides the third exception to the principle set out in *The London, Chatham and Dover Railway Company*. In *Wadsworth v Lydall* (1981), which was approved by the House of Lords in *President of India v Lips Maritime Corporation* (1987), it was decided that where it was proved that it was in the contemplation of the parties that delay in payment would involve the need to borrow and to pay interest, the court or arbitrator might allow a claim for interest under the second rule in *Hadley v Baxendale*. Authority for this proposition is also found in *Chiswell Shipping Ltd & Liberian Jaguar Transports Inc v National Iranian Tanker Co ('The World Symphony' and 'World Renown')* (1992). Two points are crucial to bear in mind. First, it is not enough to show that it is generally known that contractors will incur finance charges or interest on late payment or under certification. Second, the contractor must establish that the particular employer was aware of his particular circumstances. Once an entitlement has been established, calculation will be for the period from the date the loss was first incurred to the date of judgment or award. The rate of interest and whether interest is to be compounded or not will be assessed by reference to what was within the contemplation of the parties at the date the contract was first made.

3.39   The question of a contractor's common law right to interest on late payment was considered in *Holbeach Plant Hire Ltd v Anglian Water Authority* (1988), a decision on the ICE Conditions of Contract, 4th Edition in an amended form. The contractor was able to satisfy three conditions:

  · he had sustained loss by way of interest for financing charges;
  · the loss was caused by the employer's late certification;
  · the employer had knowledge of the facts or circumstances when he made the contract that such a loss was a not unlikely consequence of his failure to certify on time.

It is a trite observation that nowadays contractors borrow money to trade. They incur substantial penalties from the funding bank if monies due to them are not received promptly. Although the court in *Holbeach Plant Hire* was not asked to consider a JCT loss and expense claim, the court might well listen sympathetically to a contractor's claim for *Minter* interest as special damages under JCT-type contracts. Again, if the contractor suffers late or inadequate certification of his loss and expense, interest on this may be a recoverable head of claim under the second rule in *Hadley v Baxendale*. All interest calculated will, in the absence of special conditions known to the employer at the date of the contract, be simple.

3.40   Whenever a contractor makes a claim for breach of contract at
        common law, it is essential to consider the extent to which the
        contractor has mitigated his own loss, so far as it may be
        reasonable for him to do so. The position was stated as follows in
        The Law of Contract (Cheshire, Fifoot and Furmston,
        Butterworth, 12th Ed. 1991, p614):

> '[The] law does not allow a plaintiff to recover damages to
> compensate him for loss which would not have been suffered
> if he had taken reasonable steps to mitigate his loss. Whether
> the plaintiff has failed to take a reasonable opportunity of
> mitigation is a question of fact dependent upon the particular
> circumstances of each case and the burden of proving such
> failure rests upon the defendant.'

In practical terms the contractor must take positive, albeit not
unreasonable, steps to prevent his losses from mounting. He
should, for instance, make efforts to use plant which would
otherwise be idle elsewhere. If a delay is likely to be prolonged, a
contractor should cut his losses by taking off hire plant which he
has hired in specifically for the project. In *Frost v Knight* (1872) (a
breach of promise of marriage case), the court concluded in the
words of Cockburn CJ:

> '... and in assessing the damages for breach of performance a
> jury will of course take into account whatever the plaintiff has
> done, or has the means of doing, and, as a prudent man ought
> in reason to have done whereby his loss has been, or would
> have been, diminished.' (p115)

3.41   The final question to consider is why it may be beneficial to a
        contractor to claim damages for breach of contract at common
        law rather than to pursue contractual claims under the contract.
        The obvious advantage of the contractual claim is that, if accepted
        by the architect or quantity surveyor, it will mean prompt and
        regular ascertainment. Amounts ascertained will be added to sums
        due under a contractor's interim certificates. Sometimes
        contractors do not make contractual claims because they have
        failed to comply with particular notice requirements in the
        contract which act as conditions precedent to the making of a
        claim. Under JCT 80, a contractor's right to reimbursement is
        subject to the requirement that he should have made specific
        written application 'as soon as it has become, or should

reasonably have become, apparent that the regular progress of the Works has been or is likely to be materially affected [by one of the matters referred to in Clause 26·2]'.

3.42   Depending on the wording of a particular clause, the courts will make every effort to construe a clause, which would otherwise limit the time for bringing a claim, in favour of a contractor. This is in accordance with the common law *contra proferentem* rule which requires contracts to be construed in the way least favourable to the party wishing to place a meaning on a particular provision in order to restrict its obligations. On the whole, the courts tend to be reasonably tolerant in construing such phrases as 'within a reasonable time of it becoming apparent' and 'if the Contractor has at the earliest practicable opportunity notified ... that he intends to make a claim ...'.

3.43   In *Tersons Ltd v Stevenage Development Corporation* (1963), a case on the ICE Conditions of Contract 2nd Edition, Willmer LJ stated:

> '... the contractors must at least be allowed a reasonable time in which to make up their minds. Here the contractors are a limited company and that involves that, in a matter of such importance as that raised by the present case, the relevant intention must be that of the board of management.' (p68)

That said, written applications under the JCT contracts must, on the principle set out in *Merton v Leach*, accord with the following, as stated by Vinelott J:

> 'He [the Contractor] must make his application within a reasonable time; it must not be made so late that, for instance, the architect can no longer form a competent opinion on the matters on which he is required to form an opinion or satisfy himself that the Contractor had suffered the loss and expense claimed.' (p97)

3.44   Sometimes contracts do contain stringent notice provisions which cannot be side-stepped, however creative the judges. One example of the inflexibility of particular notice provisions was in *J. Crosby and Sons Ltd v Portland Urban District Council* (1967), where the court considered Clause 40(1) of the ICE Conditions of Contract 4th Edition. This provision related to suspension of the works.

Notice under Clause 40(1) had to be given within 28 days of the engineer's order to suspend the works, failing which the contractor lost his rights to extra payment under the clause. In such a situation any common law rights which are expressly preserved by the contract, or otherwise remain in existence because they are not precluded by any contract provision, may be of vital importance to a contractor. A similar example of tight time constraints which might be of concern to architects, is found in GC/Works/1, Edition 3. The contractor must give written notice immediately 'upon becoming aware that ... regular progress ... has been or is likely to be disrupted or prolonged' and further, as soon as reasonably practicable after incurring actual expense, and in any case within 56 days of incurring it, must provide details of all direct cost to the quantity surveyor for ascertainment to occur.

4 Loss and expense provisions under standard form building contracts

4.01   The standard JCT building contracts and the GC/Works government forms use different terms to describe the sums recoverable by a contractor under the 'money claims' provisions. However, subject to specific clauses being drafted so as to limit the amounts recoverable, the purpose of the 'money claims' provisions is to enable the contractor, on his compliance with certain prescribed procedures, to be reimbursed under the contract (as opposed to via common law damages claims) for the consequences of delay and disruption. What the standard form contracts do is to define the circumstances in which money claims can be made by the contractor. One example of this is Clause 26·2 of JCT 80, which is discussed in paragraphs 4.7–13.

Money claims terminology

4.02   As previously stated, JCT and GC/Works contracts use different terminology in their 'money claims' provisions. Both JCT 80 and its predecessor, JCT 63, refer to 'direct loss and/or expense', an expression which is also found in Clause 4·11 of IFC 84. In GC/Works/1, Editions 2 and 3, the terminology is quite different. There the reference is to 'expense', albeit that Editions 2 and 3 each take a different approach to the definition of 'expense'. In GC/Works/1 Edition 3 'expense' is given a restricted meaning of a type not found in the JCT contracts. Clause 46(6) states:

> 'In this Condition "expense" shall mean money expended by a Contractor, but shall not include any sum expended, or loss incurred by him by way of interest or finance charges however described.'

Curiously, a restriction similar to Clause 46(6) of GC/Works/1 Edition 3 is not found in its predecessor, Clause 53 of GC/Works/1 Edition 2.

4.03   Under JCT 80 'direct loss and/or expense' would appear to give rise to the following heads of claim:

- Loss of money which ought to have been received.
- Expenditure of money which ought not to have been made.

Legal authority suggests that 'direct loss and/or expense' is to be interpreted in accordance with the principles for the recovery of damages at common law, including the rule in *Hadley v Baxendale*, which is discussed in Section 3. The purpose of Clause 26 of JCT 80 is indicated by the side note to the standard form as printed, 'loss and expense caused by matters materially affecting regular progress of the Works'. These matters are more specifically set out in Clause 26·2. In lawyers' terms, what is recoverable is the financial loss which directly and naturally results in the ordinary course of events from any of the Clause 26·2 matters. Given that the contractor's entitlement to 'loss and/or expense' is qualified by the word 'direct', it is arguable that Clause 26 relates to those claims which, at common law, would fall under the first rule in *Hadley v Baxendale* (those arising naturally), whilst excluding claims under the second rule in *Hadley v Baxendale* (losses which are dependent upon special circumstances). 'Direct' might mean that recoverable losses are those which fall outside the category of consequential loss. Unfortunately 'consequential' is no easier to define than 'direct' for the purposes of any attempt to work back to a definition of 'direct'. In *Saint Line Ltd v Richardsons, Westgarth and Co Ltd* (1940) it was said by Atkinson J:

> 'Direct damage is that which flows naturally from the breach without other intervening cause ... The word 'consequential' is not very illuminating, as all damage is in a sense consequential, but there is a definition in the Oxford English Dictionary ... "Of the nature of a consequence, merely; not direct or immediate; eventual." It cites the definition of "consequential damages" from Wharton as: "losses or injuries which 'follow an act, but are not direct or immediate upon it'." (p103)

4.04 A line of cases, including *Croudace Construction Ltd v Cawoods Concrete Products Ltd* (1978), seemed to establish that consequential loss meant those damages recoverable under the second rule in *Hadley v Baxendale*. The meaning to be ascribed to 'direct loss and/or expense' was one of the matters in issue in *F.G. Minter Ltd v Welsh Health Technical Services Organisation* (1980), considered by Stephenson LJ:

> 'There are no grounds for giving those words [direct loss

and/or expense] any other meaning than that which they have in the case of breach of contract in a legal context [ie. apply the *Hadley v Baxendale* test]' and

'[Accordingly] the Court should apply to the interpretation of what loss or expense is direct the distinction between direct and indirect or consequential which was discussed ... in *Saint Line Limited* ... and should at least recognise that loss of profit and expenses thrown away on wages may be recoverable as direct loss or expense ...' (p14)

The meaning of 'direct' was also considered in *Wraight Ltd v P. H. & T. (Holdings) Ltd* (1968) by Megaw J, who concluded that loss of profit was not consequential or indirect loss.

'In my judgment there are no grounds for giving the words "direct loss and/or damage" ... any other meaning than that which they have, for example, in a case of breach of contract or other question of the relationship of a fault to damage in a legal context.' (p34)

Perhaps surprisingly, the Court of Session in Scotland was recently asked to consider in *Ogilvie Builders Ltd v Glasgow City Council* that the Court of Appeal had decided the case wrongly in *Minter.* It was argued, but not accepted by the Outer House of the Court of Session, that when considering the phrase 'direct loss and/or expense', it was erroneous to work out the contractual remedy provided by Clause 26 of JCT 80 by reference to *Hadley v Baxendale* and subsequent breach of contract cases where the test of recoverability of loss was reasonable foreseeability. It was wrong to equate compliance with the first rule in *Hadley v Baxendale* with satisfaction of the test of directness in Clause 26. 'Direct' was a word that was relevant in causation, whereas 'natural' involved more an element of foreseeability, of probability. The Court of Session held that although there was no mention in *Hadley v Baxendale* of the word 'direct', over the years the words 'naturally', 'directly and naturally' and 'directly' had come to be used interchangeably. It is now well established that 'direct' loss or damage is loss or damage that flows naturally in the sense of the first rule in *Hadley v Baxendale.*

4.05   On occasions the word 'consequential' has been given an extremely restrictive meaning, as found in the definition in the leading textbook, *McGregor on Damages* (15th Ed. 1988, para 26):

> 'Normal loss is that loss which every plaintiff in a like situation will suffer, the consequential loss is that loss which is special to the circumstances of the particular plaintiff.'

Under McGregor's analysis the only losses to be classified as direct and therefore recoverable by a contractor would be those immediately consequent upon the default of the employer, eg additional plant and labour resources, etc. Any loss of profit or finance charges would fall outside the definition of 'direct loss and/or expense'. There is some authority for this proposition to be found in *P. & M. Kaye Ltd v Hosier & Dickinson Ltd* (1972), where the court regarded the loss of the regular profitable use of a building, consequent upon a breach of contract by the contractor, as consequential damage. However, despite some apparent uncertainty in previous case law as to the distinction between 'direct' and 'indirect/consequential', decided cases under JCT 80 have clearly established that a contractor is entitled to recover as 'direct loss and/or expense' various items of loss of a consequential type, including head office overheads, profit and finance charges.

4.06   Unlike JCT 80, GC/Works/1 refers to 'expense' with the immediate impression of a more restricted recovery of additional monies than under the JCT contracts. Clause 9(2)(a)(i) of GC/Works/1 Edition 2 refers to 'any expense beyond that otherwise provided for in or reasonably contemplated by the Contract', while Clause 53 refers to 'any expense in performing the Contract' which the contractor 'properly and directly incurs ... or which he would not otherwise have incurred or which is beyond that otherwise provided for in or reasonably contemplated by the Contract'. Clause 9(2)(a)(ii) refers to 'cost', thereby allowing the inference to be drawn that this is something different from 'expense'. The word 'expense' is also used in GC/Works/1 Edition 3, where it is found in Clauses 43 and 46. On a common sense view the word 'expense' connotes the contractor being 'out of pocket'. It might indeed be argued that 'expense' represents direct expenditure as opposed to indirect loss, with a requirement on the contractor actually to have spent money. For instance, under Clause 46(6) '"expense" shall mean money expended by the Contractor ...'. However, cases decided by the courts have pointed to a more generous interpretation. 'Expense' can, unless its meaning is qualified, include 'cost or sacrifice involved in any course of action' (*Stratton and Others v Inland Revenue* (1957)). Indeed, GC/Works/1 Edition 3 specifically excludes the recovery of interest or finance charges except to the limited extent they are recoverable under Clause 47. However, under Edition 2, 'expense' is to be construed more widely in that it includes, amongst other items, 'interest not earned if the Contractor uses his own capital'. Authority for this is found in the PSA's *Notice to Tenderers – Valuations under Conditions 9 and 53* (C0241, July 1986).

Claims provisions under the JCT forms

4.07   With the exception of MW 80, the JCT family of main contract forms, including JCT 80 and IFC 84, have detailed provisions for the reimbursement of a contractor's direct loss and/or expense and set down specific procedures which need to be followed. Under MW 80, account is merely to be taken of direct loss and/or expense during the valuation of variations under Clause 3·6. Under Clause 26 of JCT 80 and Clause 4·11 of IFC 84 a contractor is able to recover under the terms of the contract direct loss and/or expense where the progress of his work has been materially affected by certain specified matters. These are set out in JCT 80 in the following way:

· There has been deferment of possession of the site (Clause 26·1·2); or
· The regular progress of the works or any part thereof has been or is likely to be materially affected by any of the matters listed in Clause 26·2. The matters listed in Clause 26·2 are:

Late information (26·2·1)
Opening up of work for inspection (26·2·2)
Discrepancy/divergence between the Contract Drawings and/or the Contract Bills (26·2·3)
Employer's contractors or materials supplied by the Employer (26·2·4)
Postponement (26·2·5)
Employer's failure to give possession (26·2·6)
Architect's Instructions (26·2·7)

4.08   Clause 26·2·1 refers to 'the Contractor not having received in due time necessary instructions, drawings, details or levels from the Architect'. However, before the contractor can claim a delay, he must have specifically applied in writing for such information and 'on a date which having regard to the Completion Date was neither unreasonably distant from nor unreasonably close to the date on which it was necessary for him to receive the same'. Clause 5·4 of JCT 80 sets out the time when the architect is to provide further information. This is on the basis of 'as and when from time to time may be necessary the Architect without charge to the Contractor shall provide him with [further information] ...' This anticipates that the architect, without being in breach of his duty, can issue further information in a piecemeal fashion. As to the meaning of 'as and when ... may be necessary', such wording was considered, in the context of a civil engineering form of contract, in *Neodox Ltd v Swinton and Pendlebury Borough Council* (1958). The convenience of the engineer and the order in which he decided the work should be carried out were factors to be taken into account in deciding what was a reasonable time. Under JCT contracts the contractor provides his programme to the architect (Clause 5·3·1·2). In *Wells v Army & Navy Co-operative Society* (1902) there was no contractual provision in regard to the supply by the architect to the contractor of drawings. Supply was not governed by progress on site; the contractor was entitled to receipt of drawings '... promptly upon request ...' Under both JCT 80 and IFC 84 three factors are crucial in addition to the actual physical progress of the works. These are set out by Vincent Powell-Smith in *Problems in Construction Claims* (BSP Professional Books, 1990, p102) in the following terms:

- the contractor's obligation to complete the works in accordance with the contract;
- the time necessary to organise and bring to site adequate supplies of materials, labour and plant;
- the time required for any off-site fabrication and preparation of materials.

4.09   Clause 26·2·2 of JCT 80 (Clause 4·12·2 of IFC 84) in regard to the opening up for inspection of any work cannot operate where the work in question has been prematurely covered up before inspection by the architect or building control officer.

4.10   The contractor's right to base a claim to direct loss and/or expense on 'any discrepancy in or divergence between the Contract Drawings and/or the Contract Bills' is conditional upon compliance by the contractor with Clause 2·3 of JCT 80, under which 'he shall immediately give to the Architect a written notice specifying the discrepancy or divergence, and the Architect shall issue instructions with regard thereto'. If the contractor has failed to notify the architect on the earliest occasion he finds such a discrepancy or divergence he is in breach of contract, cannot recover direct loss and/or expense and is, in theory at least, liable to pay damages to the employer.

4.11   The execution of work by persons engaged by the employer under Clause 26·2·4 (Clause 4·12·3 of IFC 84) may relate to work carried out by statutory undertakers.

4.12   Postponement of work under Clause 26·2·5 of JCT 80 (Clause 4·12·5 of IFC 84) cannot cover the employer's failure to give possession of the site. The employer is under an obligation to give possession of the site on the date stated in the Contract Appendix subject to any right to defer such possession. Although the architect is by reason of Clause 23·2 of JCT 80 permitted to issue instructions in regard to the postponement of any work, he should obviously remain mindful of the contractor's possible right to direct loss and/or expense under Clause 26. It is sometimes suggested that instructions to postpone may be given by implication. An architect's nomination of a sub-contractor on the particular sub-contractor's 'quotation ... and tendering conditions' with a consequent delay to the contractor's original planned programme of work, was, for the purposes of Clause 21(2) of JCT 63, a postponement. In the words of Megaw LJ in *M. Harrison & Co (Leeds) Ltd v Leeds City Council* (1980):

> 'In the absence of some valid reason to the contrary, that instruction would necessarily, in my view, operate as a postponement instruction ... for it would mean that the contractor was instructed to agree with the sub-contractor that the contractors' intended concrete work should be postponed for some 11 months while the sub-contractor did the steelwork in accordance with [his] Condition. While the variation order does not expressly use the word "postpone" or expressly give instructions to postpone, the order to make a contract with sub-contractors containing a condition which necessarily involves postponement would, to my mind, make this a postponement instruction within the contemplation of the condition.' (p132)

4.13   As far as the architect's instructions for variations are concerned (Clause 26·2·7 of JCT 80; Clause 4·12·7 of IFC 84) the architect, contract administrator or quantity surveyor is permitted to ascertain separately the delay and disruption effects of a variation for which financial provision has not already been made under the specific variation clauses. However, in the analysis of the delay and disruption caused by a particular variation, the architect should also bear in mind the impact on the contractor's programming of omissions to the works and other delays which are referable to the contractor's own behaviour, including the rectification of defective work under Clauses 8·3 and 8·4 of JCT 80.

4.14   Similar 'trigger' events which provide an entitlement to direct loss and/or expense are also found in Clause 4·11(a) and (b) and Clause 4·12 of IFC 84, although there are a number of minor differences, if only in the terminology. The question of architect's/contract administrator's instructions is dealt with somewhat differently from JCT 80 under Clause 4·12·7 of IFC 84. Also included in IFC 84 is a Clause 4·12·8 which allows the contractor direct loss and/or expense where certain work was included with an approximate quantity which subsequently proved not to have been 'a reasonably accurate forecast of the quantity of work required'.

4.15   Many contractors believe that their entitlement to claim direct loss and/or expense is inextricably linked to any entitlement they may possess to an extension of time. Unfortunately this misconception is fostered in part by the juxtapositioning of Clause 25 (extensions of time) and Clause 26 (direct loss and/or expense) in JCT 80. Under IFC 84 they are separated, with extensions of time to be found in Clauses 2·3 to 2·5. The reasons why a contractor may be entitled to claim direct loss and/or expense (described in JCT 80 as Matters) are not precisely the same as those situations (referred to in JCT 80 and IFC 84 respectively as Relevant Events and Events) in which an entitlement to an extension of time might arise. In fact, taken at face value, the direct loss and/or expense provisions are more narrowly set out. It is easily illustrated that an extension of time entitlement may sometimes be irrelevant for the ascertainment of direct loss and/or expense. Only critical path delay, ie delay that is critical to completion, establishes a right to an extension of time. However, delay which is outside the critical path may nevertheless entitle the contractor to direct loss and/or expense.

4.16   The following examples illustrate the lack of any automatic link
        between Clause 25 and Clause 26 of JCT 80. There are no direct
        loss and/or expense implications in the following situations:

        25·4·2   Exceptionally adverse weather conditions
        25·4·3   Clause 22 perils
        25·4·4   Nomination of sub-contractors or suppliers
        25·4·7   Delay on the part of nominated sub-contractors or
                     suppliers
        25·4·8   Delays caused by the supply of the employer's own goods
        25·4·9   Statutory powers
        25·4·10 Inability to get labour or materials
        25·4·11 Statutory undertakers carrying out statutory obligations

4.17   JCT contract forms require the contractor to submit a written
        notice of application as a condition precedent to any
        reimbursement of direct loss and/or expense. This obligation is
        found in the opening words to Clause 26·1 of JCT 80:

> 'If the Contractor makes written application to the Architect
> stating that he has incurred or is likely to incur direct loss
> and/or expense in the execution of this Contract ...',

        with a similar provision to be found in Clause 4·11 of IFC 84.
        However, there are certain differences in the way in which Clause
        26 of JCT 80 and Clause 4·11 of IFC 84 are set out so as to make
        separate consideration of both necessary in a number of regards.

4.18   The requirement on the contractor to submit a written notice as a
        condition precedent to the reimbursement of direct loss and/or
        expense was clearly established in *Merton v Leach* (1985). That said,
        there is little or no guidance in the JCT contracts as to the form of
        the written application. Presumably the application should be
        sufficiently detailed so as to persuade the architect under JCT 80
        that 'the regular progress of the Works or of any part thereof has
        been or [was] likely to be affected', although Clause 26·1·2 appears
        to place an onus on the architect to request from the contractor any
        additional information reasonably necessary for the architect to
        form an opinion as to whether or not the 'regular progress of the
        Works' has been or is likely to be materially affected by the Matters
        referred to in Clause 26·2. How detailed an application is will
        depend very much on the circumstances, including the time available
        to the contractor, the contractor's general experience and the quality

of his records. The more detailed the initial application, the more obviously persuasive it will be in the architect's mind. Case law provides little guidance as to the manner in which an application should be set out. In *Rees & Kirby Ltd v Swansea City Council* (1983) the Court was called upon to consider a written notice under Clause 11(6) of JCT 63. Goff LJ stated in his judgment:

> 'It seems to me that, in the ongoing relationship that exists between a Contractor and an Architect carrying out their functions under a contract in this form, a sensible and not too technical attitude must be adopted with regard to the form of such an application.' (p20)

4.19   In the later case of *Merton v Leach*, Vinelott J concluded, in regard to the format of the contractor's written application, as follows:

> 'The question of principle is whether an application under Clauses 24(1) or 11(6) must contain sufficient information to enable the Architect to form an opinion on the questions of whether (in the case of Clause 24) the regular progress of the work has been materially affected by an event within the numbered sub-paragraphs of Clause 24 or (in the case of Clause 11(6)) whether the variation has caused direct loss and/or expense of the kind described and in either case whether loss and/or expense ... is such that it would not be reimbursed by payment under other provisions of the contract or (in the case of Clause 11(6)) under Clause 11(4).' (p96)

4.20   Further, Vinelott J emphasised that it would not necessarily be enough simply to make what might be described as a 'bare' application which would satisfy the requirements of Clause 11(6) or Clause 24(1). Any application had to be set out in sufficient detail to allow the architect to do what he was required to do. It had to be sufficiently particularised to enable the architect to form an opinion as to whether or not the contractor had incurred or was likely to incur any direct loss and/or expense to be ascertained under the contract. He stated:

> 'If [the Contractor] makes a claim but fails to do so with sufficient particularity to enable the Architect to perform his duty ... he may lose any right to recover loss or expense under [Clause 11(6) or Clause 24(1)] and may not be in a position to complain that the Architect was in breach of his duty.' (p104)

However, it would be unwise for any architect to place undue emphasis on a contractor's failure at the outset to provide sufficient details of his alleged entitlement. Under Clause 26·1·2 of JCT 80 the architect may ask for further information to be provided so that he may form an opinion on the merits of the contractor's application.

4.21   The contractor's general duty to co-operate with the architect or contract administrator in the ascertainment of direct loss and/or expense was clearly stated by Vinelott J in *Merton v Leach*:

> 'The Contractor must clearly co-operate with the Architect or the Quantity Surveyor giving such particulars of the loss or expenses claimed as the Architect or Quantity Surveyor may require to enable him to ascertain the extent of that loss or expense; clearly the Contractor cannot complain that the Architect has failed to ascertain or to instruct the Quantity Surveyor to ascertain the amount of direct loss or expense attributed to one of the specified heads if he has failed adequately to answer a request for information which the Architect requires if he or the Quantity Surveyor is to carry out that task.' (p104)

4.22   The contractor has a responsibility, both under Clause 26·1·1 of JCT 80 and under Clause 4·11 of IFC 84, to act promptly in advising the architect or contract administrator that direct loss and/or expense has arisen or is likely to arise. Under Clause 26·1·1 of JCT 80 the contractor's application is to be made 'as soon as it has become, or should reasonably have become, apparent ... that the regular progress of the Works or of any part thereof has been or [was] likely to be affected ...', whereas under Clause 4·11 of IFC 84 the written application is to be made to the architect or contract administrator by the contractor 'within a reasonable time of it becoming apparent ... that the Contractor has incurred or is likely to incur direct loss and/or expense ...' What is a reasonable time will depend on all the circumstances of the case, unless a particular clause is specifically drafted so as to set a definite time limit for the bringing of claims. Occasionally it might be argued that the contractor has been guilty of delay to the extent that it has become too difficult or even impossible for the employer realistically to carry out any ascertainment. In *Tersons Ltd v Stevenage Development Corporation* (1963) the notice provisions in the ICE Conditions of Contract 2nd Edition were considered by Willmer LJ as follows:

> '... the Contractors must at least be allowed a reasonable time in which to make up their minds. Here the Contractors are a limited company and that involves that, in a matter of such importance as that raised by the present case, the relevant intention must be that of the board of management.' (p69)

In *Tersons* the notice had to be given 'as soon as practicable', but any words of the type 'within a reasonable time' are to be construed in a similar manner.

4.23   Once the architect or contract administrator has received the contractor's written application he must form an opinion whether or not the provisions for the ascertainment of direct loss and/or expense are to be operated. Here there is a difference of terminology between JCT 80 and IFC 84. Under Clause 26·1 of JCT 80 the architect's opinion relates to whether or not 'the regular progress of the Works or of any part thereof has been or is likely to be materially affected', whereas under Clause 4·11 of IFC 84 the architect's or contract administrator's opinion is whether or not 'the Contractor has incurred or is likely to incur direct loss and/or expense'. The position under IFC 84 reflects that under Clause 24(1) of JCT 63.

4.24   Under JCT 80 and IFC 84, unlike under JCT 63, the contractor must submit to the architect, contract administrator or quantity surveyor any necessary further information required to enable an opinion to be formed as to the existence of a possible claim under Clause 26 or Clause 4·11.

4.25   If the architect or contract administrator forms an opinion in the contractor's favour that the grounds for a claim have been made out, further information will then be required to enable either the architect or the quantity surveyor to carry out the ascertainment of direct loss and/or expense. Under Clause 26·1·3 of JCT 80 the contractor is obliged to submit 'upon request such details of such loss and/or expense as are reasonably necessary for such ascertainment as aforesaid'. A similar provision is not found in IFC 84 although the general requirement in Clause 4·11 for the contractor to supply 'in support of his application ... such information required by the Architect/Contract Administrator or the Quantity Surveyor as is reasonably necessary for the purpose of this clause' is an adequate substitute.

4.26   As to the amount of supporting detail a contractor should provide
to assist the process of ascertainment, the same degree of common
sense should pervade the exercise as is required of the contractor
in establishing his initial right to claim. In *Merton v Leach* the
following comments of Vinelott J, although made in regard to
written applications under Clause 24 of JCT 63, are also relevant
to the formulation and consideration of all notices from the
contractor under Clause 26 of JCT 80 and Clause 4·11 of IFC 84:

> 'The Contractor must act reasonably; his application must be
> framed with sufficient particularity to enable the Architect to
> do what he is required to do. He must make his application
> within a reasonable time; it must not be made so late that, for
> instance, the Architect can no longer form a competent
> opinion on the matters on which he is required to form an
> opinion or satisfy himself that the Contractor has suffered the
> loss or expense claimed. But in considering whether the
> Contractor has acted reasonably and with reasonable
> expedition it must be borne in mind that the Architect is not a
> stranger to the work and may in some cases have a very
> detailed knowledge of the progress of the work and of the
> Contractor's planning. Moreover, it is always open to the
> Architect to call for further information either before or in the
> course of investigating a claim.' (p97)

4.27   The architect, whether described as such or as contract
administrator, must be acutely aware of his role and
responsibilities. Under both Clause 26·1 of JCT 80 and Clause
4·11 of IFC 84 the original written application is made to the
architect or, in the case of IFC 84, to the contract administrator.
Second, it is the architect's responsibility to form an opinion as to
whether or not 'the regular progress of the Works has been
materially affected' (JCT 80) or (IFC 84) that 'the Contractor has
incurred or is likely to incur direct loss and/or expense'. Third, it is
again the architect's duty to request any additional information
required to form that opinion. Fourth, it is only the obligation to
ascertain the contractor's direct loss and/or expense which can be
delegated to the quantity surveyor. Under Clause 26·1 of JCT 80
'the Architect from time to time thereafter shall ascertain, or shall
instruct the Quantity Surveyor to ascertain, the amount of such
loss and/or expense which has been or is being incurred by the
Contractor', while under Clause 4·11 of IFC 84 '[then] the
Architect/the Contract Administrator shall ascertain, or shall

instruct the Quantity Surveyor to ascertain, such loss and expense incurred ...' Given the quantity surveyor's usually significant role in the assessment of claims generally and ascertainment of loss and expense, once the grounds for a claim have been established, information in regard to the detailed loss and expense can be supplied direct to the quantity surveyor. Provision for this is found under Clause 26·1·3 of JCT 80 and Clause 4·11 of IFC 84.

4.28   The obligation on the architect or contract administrator to operate Clause 26 of JCT 80 or Clause 4·11 of IFC 84 is absolute. The employer will be liable in damages for breach by the architect of his duty, and this is so whether the architect is an employee, as in the case of a local authority, or an independent consultant retained by the employer for a particular project. Although Clause 26 of JCT 80 and Clause 4·11 of IFC 84 are in terms that 'the Architect shall ...', in effect it is the employer's responsibility to ensure that the architect or contract administrator operates the provisions of the contract including the loss and expense clauses. Such a proposition is implicit in the judgment in *Merton v Leach* and also follows from the judgment of the Court of Appeal in *Croudace Ltd v London Borough of Lambeth* (1986). There, the local authority employer under JCT 63 (July 1977 revision) failed to appoint a new architect when the architect named in the Articles of Agreement retired. The architect's failure to ascertain or instruct the quantity surveyor to ascertain the amount of direct loss and/or expense suffered or incurred by the contractor (which he was not in a position to do) was a breach of contract for which the employer was liable in common law damages, provided that the contractor could establish that he had suffered damage as a result of the breach. The only defence open to the local authority was to demonstrate that there were no matters in respect of which the contractor would have been entitled to claim loss and expense. In the words of Balcombe LJ:

> 'Unless it can be successfully maintained by Lambeth that there are no matters in respect of which Croudace are entitled to claim for loss and expense under Conditions 11(6) and 24(1)(e) [what is now Clause 26], it necessarily follows that Croudace must have suffered some damage as a result of there being no one to ascertain the amount of their claim.' (pp34–5)

Claims provisions under GC/Works/1

4.29   Under GC/Works/1 Edition 3 there is an entirely different claims
'culture' from that existing under the JCT-type contracts. The
contractor is entitled to recover in prescribed circumstances 'any
expense which he would not otherwise have incurred'. The situations
set out are more limited than under JCT contracts. They are:

- other work being carried out concurrently by the Authority
  (Clause 46(1)(a));
- delay in possession of the Site or part of it (Clause 46(1)(b));
- expense incurred as a result of the matters specified in Clause
  46(2) which unavoidably result in the regular progress of the
  works or of any part of them being materially disrupted or
  prolonged.

4.30   The matters referred to in Clause 46(2) are:

(a) any information etc. to be provided by the project manager
    (PM);
(b) the execution of any work or supply of any Thing which is not
    the responsibility of the contractor or otherwise caused by
    him; or
(c) any direction or instruction from the Authority or the project
    manager for nominated persons under Clause 63 to be given
    access to the Site.

The 'expense' must be one 'which is beyond that provided for or
reasonably contemplated by the Contract' and it must be 'properly
and directly' incurred and be of a type which the contractor would
not otherwise have incurred.

4.31   There are a number of onerous conditions precedent to any claim
under GC/Works/1 Edition 3. These are found in Clause 46(3).

- Although it is not specifically stated that any notice needs to be
  in writing, the contractor must, immediately upon becoming
  aware that the regular progress of the works has been or is
  likely to be disrupted or prolonged, give notice to the PM
  specifying the circumstances and stating that the contractor
  expects there to be an increase in the contract sum.

- As soon as reasonably practicable after incurring the actual expense, and in any case within 56 days of incurring it, the contractor must provide the quantity surveyor with full details of it and evidence that all expenses directly result from one of the specified events (Clause 46(3)).

- Similarly, the quantity surveyor is obliged to react promptly and is obliged by Clause 46(5) to notify his decision to the contractor within 28 days of receipt of the relevant information from him.

These tight timescales are however subject to alteration by agreement under Clause 1(4). Once ascertainment has occurred, such amounts as are ascertained will be included on account in the next monthly advance in accordance with Clause 48(2)(d).

4.32   What are specifically excluded from Clause 46 are interest or finance charges (Clause 46(6)). Finance charges are only recoverable in the manner and to the extent set out in Clause 47. It is necessary that:

- the employer, the PM or quantity surveyor has failed to comply with any time limit specified in the contract (Clause 47(1)(a)); or
- the quantity surveyor varies any decision of his which is noted to the contractor (Clause 47(1)(b)).

Unlike JCT contracts, Clause 47(2) sets out the principle on which finance charges are to be paid. This is as a percentage of the sums which would have been paid to the contractor at a rate of 1% over the rate charged during the relevant period by the Bank of England for lending money to the clearing banks. They are added automatically to any other monies due to the contractor. In the calculation of finance charges the quantity surveyor is to take into account any overpayment to the contractor in the circumstances prescribed by Clause 1(b) of Clause 47(4). GC/Works/1 is absolutely clear as to the circumstances where finance charges will not be paid. Clause 47(5) excludes as follows:

- any act, neglect or default of the contractor or any of his sub-contractors;
- any failure by the contractor or any of his sub-contractors to supply the PM or the quantity surveyor with any relevant information; or
- any disagreement about the Final Account.

Clause 47(6) is an extremely important provision. Although the contractor's right to make claims for common law damages is not generally excluded under GC/Works/1, the effect of Clause 47(6) is to preclude the operation of the second rule in *Hadley v Baxendale* to the extent that a contractor might attempt to claim interest as 'special damages'.

4.33 The purpose of this Section has been to outline the contractual provisions under which a contractor can claim additional monies under the contract in prescribed circumstances from a legal viewpoint. Clearly a major consideration for any contractor will be the manner in which he presents his claim. There are three areas of particular concern. These are:

- the status of global claims;
- the calculation of head office overheads;
- the calculation of finance charges.

A detailed analysis of all these issues is found in Sections 6 and 7.

5   Cause and effect

5.01   Whenever a claimant seeks a remedy at law, whether in arbitration or litigation, he is obliged to particularise his case. Adequate particularisation may also assist the process of negotiating an appropriate settlement. The claimant must particularise his claim to a degree of sufficiency that allows the respondent properly to understand the case he is to answer. The respondent must be provided with sufficient detail in the Points of Claim to enable him to defend his position. It is for the claimant to show that he has been wronged, that the wrongdoing caused him damage, and that the damage resulted in the claimant suffering a direct loss.

5.02   To satisfy fully the obligations placed upon him by the law, the claimant must show that the defendant owed him a duty or an obligation, that the defendant failed in that duty or obligation and that as a direct result he, the claimant, suffered damage. The claimant is then expected to prove the financial implications of that damage by using reasonable calculations.

Existence of an obligation

5.03   The claimant must show that the respondent owed him some duty. For the purposes of contractual claims, as opposed to those in negligence or *quantum meruit*, this means that firstly the claimant must show that there is a legally binding contract between the parties creating rights and obligations. It is then for the claimant to show that incorporated into that contract, either expressly or impliedly, are terms and conditions that give rise to an obligation or duty on the part of the respondent which has been breached. The construction industry is notorious for either completing the contract agreement late or never completing the agreement at all. Many cases reaching the courts have as their first issues the questions:

- Was there an agreement on the contract terms?
- If so, what terms are incorporated into the agreement?
- If there is no contract in existence on what basis is the contractor to be reimbursed?

It is a sad reflection on the industry's procedures that judicial intervention is so often needed on so fundamental an issue. Where a standard form of contract is the basis of the parties' agreement then the relevant duties and obligations are those set out in the clauses of the relevant standard form as added to by common law implied terms. These were discussed in Sections 3 and 4.

Breach of an obligation

5.04   Having established that the respondent has certain defined obligations towards the claimant under the terms of the contract, the claimant must show which of these obligations has or have been breached. It is also necessary for him to show when and how they were breached; a simple accusation is insufficient. This step is vital both for breaches which have an agreed procedure for their resolution within the contract clauses (eg delay), and others (eg non-payment) which, in the absence of agreement, have to be remedied by a court or arbitrator.

Damage arising from a breach

5.05   Once it has been established that an obligation has been breached, the claimant must then ordinarily show that damage of a particular value has resulted directly from the breach. The major exception to this rule is pre-agreed, or liquidated and ascertained damages. In the case of liquidated and ascertained damages the parties agree beforehand the consequence of a breach and impose the financial remedy without further assessment or proof of loss being necessary once the 'trigger' event has occurred. If the damages are not agreed in advance, then the damage must be proven. It is worth noting that not all breaches cause damage, though it is often asserted by claimants that every breach causes damage. Architects should ensure that this step is not overlooked when assessing or formulating claims, as it is common practice for claims practitioners to leap straight from proving a breach to attaching a loss to it. In assessing delay to a contractor, as opposed to disruption, it is essential to consider the effect of any 'float' in the contractor's programme. In *Glenlion Construction Ltd v The Guinness Trust* (1987) it was held that whilst a contractor was entitled to complete ahead of the contractual completion date, there was no obligation on the employer positively to assist him in this. A unilateral decision to accelerate by the contractor does not create a right to prolongation costs. It was confirmed by the

Official Referee in *J. F. Finnegan Ltd v Sheffield City Council* (1988) that the earliest date upon which any entitlement to prolongation costs could accrue was the contract completion date.

Recovery of losses

5.06 The reason for seeking a financial remedy under the contract, or damages from a court or arbitrator, is either to recover losses or avoid financial penalties. If a claimant feels strongly about proving a breach that has no financial implications he may still pursue it, but the costs of so doing may not be fully recovered. The more usual case is one where the claimant seeks his out-of-pocket expenses. To recover successfully the losses incurred the claimant will have to prove that the losses were reasonable and that they inevitably followed the breach. There is also a common law obligation on the suffering party to mitigate his losses. The claimant's obligation was neatly described by Asquith LJ in *Victoria Laundry (Windsor) Ltd v Newman Industries Ltd* (1949):

> 'It is well settled that the governing purpose of damages is to put the party whose rights have been violated in the same position, so far as money can do, as if his rights had been observed.' (p539)

Some claimants seek to improve their situation, but this is not the intention of the standard form contracts or of the common law. Claims for delay are usually based on a comparison between the contractor's anticipated and as-built programmes for the works. The underlying fallacy is the automatic assumption that the contractor's programme was ever feasible. Even if the contractor can show his programme to have been viable, the measurement of actual performance against anticipated performance is difficult, not least because of the impact of concurrent delays, which are discussed in Section 3. For less complex projects a bar chart of actual progress for the different trades can be superimposed on the original programme. A more sophisticated approach is often required, and perhaps one of the planning software packages can be utilised in these instances. It is essential to distinguish between those events which have a critical path significance and those that do not. A notable example is the release of design drawings which may or may not have a critical path impact.

Global claims

5.07   By following the steps outlined in paragraphs 5.04–6 the necessary
        linkage between cause and effect can usually be established.
        Failure to demonstrate this linkage can be fatal to a claim, given
        the very strict rules that apply to the presentation of pleadings for
        use in arbitration and litigation. In *Wharf Properties Ltd and
        Another v Eric Cumine Associates (No.2)* (1991) Lord Oliver
        stated that compliance with Order 18 of the Rules of the Supreme
        Court, which defines the method of setting out legal pleadings,
        required:

> 'a plaintiff to plead his case with such particularity as is
> sufficient to alert the opposite party to the case which is going
> to be made against him at the trial ... The failure even to
> attempt to specify any discernible nexus between the wrong
> alleged and the consequent delay provides, to use [Counsel's]
> phrase, "no agenda" for the trial.' (p126)

Global claims, also known as rolled-up and total loss claims, often
fail to establish this nexus. No attempt is made to find a link, and
the global claim becomes a lazy claimant's way of seeking
reimbursement. Certain claims consultants hailed *Wharf Properties*
as the death of global claims. This was a gross overstatement. The
circumstances where a global claim may succeed are set out in
paragraphs 5.10–13 together with the dangers inherent in such an
approach. What Lord Oliver did in *Wharf Properties* was to
distinguish the case from *J. Crosby and Sons Ltd v Portland Urban
District Council* (1967) and *London Borough of Merton v Stanley
Hugh Leach Ltd* (1985). These two cases were authority for the
judge's or arbitrator's right to award a wrap-up sum in regard to
particular heads of claim which were dependent upon a complex
interaction between the consequences of a number of events so as
to make an accurate apportionment difficult. *Wharf Properties*, on
the other hand, related to a claimant's duty to plead his case with
such particularity as is necessary to alert the opposite party to the
case he will need to answer at trial. On the face of the pleadings
there was no real attempt to specify the factual consequences of
alleged breaches of contract.

5.08   The simplest form of global claim is represented by the naive
        formula:

Total costs incurred by the Claimant = £1,000,000.00

less:	Contract Value and		
	Recovery on Variations, etc.	=	£800,000.00
	Claim for loss and expense	=	£200,000.00

Of course, global claims are dressed up in many different ways, but when properly analysed, they fail to identify each and every event and establish the nexus between each event and the financial loss.

5.09   A global claim will usually be presented in one of three ways. First, it may assert that there is no contract, or that the contract terms are invalid for want of proper incorporation. The claim will then suggest that the court or arbitrator should allow a reasonable price for the work done. This is often referred to by lawyers as a *quantum meruit* assessment. The second approach is that, upon realising that to have the contract swept away is unlikely, the claimant will base the claim on vague allegations of the respondent's failures or other deficiencies. The claimant may list a variety of allegations, often poorly particularised, some of which are valid and some which are clearly invalid. Although there is no firm evidence linking cause and effect it is hoped that a judge or arbitrator will see the list, and, believing that there is no smoke without fire, make a favourable award. The third, and perhaps most common, approach is to be specific and precise in proving the breaches, provide masses of evidence in support of the allegations, but then to submit an unparticularised financial claim that fails to identify which allegation caused which loss. Claims consultants usually cite case law to justify this approach and often rely upon the case of *J. Crosby and Sons Ltd v Portland Urban District Council* (1967).

5.10   In *Crosby*, the arbitrator had made a supplemental award in respect of a number of items where money could not be specifically allocated because individual causes could not be identified. Donaldson J confirmed, on appeal, that the arbitrator was empowered to make such an award. In upholding the award he said:

'I can see no reason why he [the arbitrator] should not recognise the realities of the situation and make individual awards in respect of those parts of individual items of the claim which can be dealt with in isolation and a supplementary award in respect of the remainder of these claims as a composite whole.' (p136)

It should be noted that in *Crosby* the claimant had already satisfied the court as to the respondent's liability for the delays and so the decision related only to the allocation of damages to those heads of liability. This approach was also adopted by Vinelott J in *Merton v Leach*, when he indicated that failure by a claimant to attempt to attribute a loss to a particular breach was unacceptable:

> '... a rolled-up award can only be made in a case where the loss or expense attributable to each head of claim cannot really strictly be separated ... and where apart from that practical impossibility the conditions which have to be satisfied before the award can be made have been satisfied in relation to each head of claim.' (p102)

In the more recent case of *Mid Glamorgan County Council v J. Devonald Williams & Partner* (1992), Mr Recorder Tackaberry QC, sitting as an Official Referee on the defendants' application to strike out the plaintiff's claim because of an alleged lack of particularisation, reviewed the existing case law and suggested the following guidelines:

(i)   Where delay or damage is proved and all of the conditions applicable to every such event have been satisfied, but it is impossible for the plaintiff to divide the financial loss between the various heads of claim, then the plaintiff may still succeed.

(ii) Where there has been delay or damage but the plaintiff cannot show or does not try to show precisely what caused each event and how it affected the outcome for each event, then he will probably fail.

5.11   If the claim falls under (ii) above, the claimant may fail to get to the hearing stage as the respondent may be granted a striking out order which would prevent the claimant from pursuing the claim in that particular format and perhaps at all.

5.12   Should the claim satisfy (i) above, the claimant may still fail if he cannot separate out the losses incurred as a result of his own inadequacies. In his book, *Construction Contracts: Principles and*

Policies in Tort and Contract (Sweet & Maxwell, 1986) Ian Duncan Wallace QC helpfully points out that global or total loss claims often ignore the hours that are inevitably lost on every contract due to weather, labour shortages, poor supervision, bad site organisation and faulty estimating. In his view, if the claimant has only provided total loss evidence, ie all losses arose as a result of the respondent's breaches, and the respondent can show that some of the losses are the claimant's fault, then a court or arbitrator will have an insurmountable difficulty in finding for the claimant to the extent that the claim may be rejected in its entirety.

5.13   In summary, a well-evidenced claim that properly establishes cause and effect and reasonably quantifies the losses for each event will probably succeed. Such a claim may also succeed on those items of quantification that are rolled up, provided the claimant has demonstrated that this method of claims presentation was only adopted because of the impossibility of completely disentangling and identifying individually the financial consequences of a number of interlinking circumstances. In the words of Vinelott J in *Merton v Leach*:

> 'If application is made ... for reimbursement of direct loss and/or expense attributable to more than one head of claim and at a time when the loss and expense comes to be ascertained it is impracticable to disentangle ... the parts directly attributable to each head of claim, then provided of course that the contractor has not unreasonably delayed in making his claim and so has himself created the difficulty the Architect must ascertain the global loss directly attributable to the causes ...' (p102)

A claim that relies exclusively on global or total loss methodology is likely to fail.

6 Loss and expense

6.01 Complex projects inevitably produce complex financial accounts. Traditionally, the costs incurred by the contractor are recovered by one of two methods: the final account, or the loss and expense claim.

6.02 The final account should be simple enough to agree as it will contain only the following straightforward items:

- the contract price;
- adjustments for extra or reduced works;
- adjustment of prime cost and provisional sums;
- evaluation of dayworks;
- evaluation of the consequences of price escalation on materials and labour/fluctuations.

However, nothing is entirely predictable and there are often disputes on some or all of these items. The main points of contention seem to arise from the evaluation of the cost of extra work, the definition of daywork, and the operation of the price escalation clauses.

Variations

6.03 There is a large degree of similarity in the approach of the various standard form contracts to the valuation of additional or omitted work. These universal principles are:

(i) Where instructed work is of similar character, is executed in similar conditions and does not significantly change the quantity, then contract rates shall be used.

(ii) Where the work is of similar character but is not executed in similar conditions and/or the quantity differs, then the contract rates are to be adjusted to allow for the differences.

(iii) Where the work differs in character then fair rates are applied.

6.04 In those cases where the instructed work is to be valued by measurement, using one of the three rules above, then the contractor will try to show that the characteristics of the work are different. This will leave the contractor free to use rates other than those in the contract bills. In many instances the contractor will have a sound argument. Where small quantities are ordered later the discounts are often lost. Extra plasterwork at high level is more costly to carry out than at low level. The contractor may also find that the timing of the extra work causes disturbance to the progress of the works or perhaps it will require plant that has been off-hired. The contractor is well advised to incorporate all such items, as well as additional preliminary costs and overheads, into the variation account. Variation costs are usually more readily certified by the employer's representatives. Those costs that are not recovered in the variation account, eg the disruption caused by variations, may find their way into a loss and expense claim.

6.05   Where work is incapable of valuation by measurement, then the daywork rates incorporated into the contract are used to value the labour, plant and materials on a reimbursable basis.

Price escalation

6.06   In times of high inflation it is important that contractors seek reimbursement for the inflationary price increases that affect their costs during the contract period. This is achieved in one of two ways. First, the contractor may allow a fixed price addition to his price as a non-adjustable risk item. Second, the employer may adjust tender base date prices to suit the period in which the work is carried out, usually utilising an agreed formula. There are seldom disagreements in this area unless the contract works overrun or the programmed sequence of the works is severely dislocated. When this happens the resultant costs will often be included in a claim for loss and expense.

Loss and expense claims

6.07   In Section 1 a number of reasons why claims arise were discussed. These may include the financial consequences of relevant events giving rise to extensions of time under the contract, other loss-bearing contract clauses and breaches of contract by the employer. Paragraphs 6.08–30 consider how such losses should be calculated and evaluated.

6.08   The JCT terminology, direct loss and/or expense, is not defined in the standard form contracts. Any assistance as to its meaning is derived from case law. This is discussed in Section 4. Conventionally, 'direct loss and/or expense' is deemed to cover those items of expenditure that arise from the progress of the works being materially affected by an act or omission of the employer or his agents (to paraphrase Clause 26 of JCT 80).

6.09   An application for reimbursement of direct loss and/or expense will usually contain one or more of the following heads of claim:

- Site overheads or preliminaries
- Head office costs
- Profit
- Inflation
- Loss of productivity or acceleration costs
- Finance charges
- Costs of preparing the claim

PRELIMINARIES

6.10   The site overhead or preliminary costs are usually readily resolved. Preliminaries include site set-up costs, time-related costs, and demobilisation costs. A three week extension of time will clearly affect the time-related costs (site staff, cabins, telephones, light, security, rates, etc) but will rarely affect the set-up or demobilisation costs. Once the time-related costs are established, then the calculation should be a simple one. The rule is that the contractor should be fully reimbursed for the expenditure of necessary additional costs. To value this entitlement it may not be appropriate for the preliminary costs in the contract bills simply to be adjusted pro rata. In a period of delay the contractor may need more or fewer staff and more or less accommodation than he properly allowed for in the tender. It is for the architect to decide on the facts of each case, probably in conjunction with the quantity surveyor, whether the claimed costs are appropriate.

HEAD OFFICE COSTS

6.11   Head office costs are a little trickier to value and recover. Government bodies which use the GC/Works/1 forms often argue that a site overrun does not have any effect on the costs of running the head office. This is clearly an unrealistic view. In many contracting organisations the head office exists solely to support the site operations. The accounts department pays the wages of operatives and staff engaged in dealing with the effects of prolongation; the managers and directors allocate time to deal with the problems arising from site delays, and the purchasing department procures additional plant and extends the rental period for cabins and certain other facilities. Of course, it can be argued that the head office and its staff would incur those costs anyway, but this is not how the legal commentators generally regard the recovery of such costs. In most contracting organisations the overheads are budgeted as a percentage of planned turnover. If work on one site is prolonged, then the staff are not able to work elsewhere to create that turnover or its attached overhead. In short, it is generally accepted that head office overheads are a legitimate head of claim. In the words of the Official Referee in *J.F. Finnegan Ltd v Sheffield City Council* (1988):

> '... it is generally accepted that, on principle, the Contractor who is delayed in completing a contract due to the default of his Employer, may properly have a claim for Head Office or off site overheads during the period of delay on the basis that the workforce, but for the delay, might have had the opportunity of being employed on another contract which would have had the effect of funding the overheads during the overrun period.' (p126)

The contractor must first prove that had his resources not been engaged on the overrun of the project in question he would in fact have deployed his resources elsewhere to fund his overheads. Such a task is not easily accomplished, although the courts have often displayed a certain tolerance towards the contractor's duty. Two cases are illustrative of the courts' approach. In *Peak Construction (Liverpool) Ltd v McKinney Foundations Ltd* (1970) Salmon LJ said:

> '... possibly some evidence as to what the organisation consisted of, what part of the head office is being referred to, and what they were doing at the material times could be of help. Moreover, it is possible, I suppose, that an Official Referee might think it useful to have an analysis of the yearly turnover from, say, 1962 up to say 1969, so if the case is put before him on the basis that work was lost during 1966 and 1967 by reason of the Plaintiffs being engaged upon completion of this block, and therefore not being free to take on any other

work, he would be helped in forming an assessment of any loss of profit sustained by the Plaintiffs.' (p122)

In *Tate & Lyle Food and Distribution Ltd v Greater London Council* (1981) it was held that the plaintiff could in principle recover damages for managerial and supervisory expenses directly attributable to the defendant's breaches. On the facts of the particular case the plaintiff's claim failed because of its failure to keep proper records and supporting documentation. In the words of Forbes J:

> 'I have no doubt that the expenditure of managerial time in remedying an actionable wrong done to a trading concern can properly form the subject matter of a head of special damage ... I would also accept that it must be extremely difficult to quantify. But modern office arrangements permit of the recording of the time spent by managerial staff on particular projects. I do not believe that it would have been impossible for the Plaintiffs in this case to have kept some record to show the extent to which their trading routine was disturbed by the necessity for continual dredging sessions ... While I am satisfied that this head of damage can properly be claimed, I am not prepared to advance into an area of pure speculation when it comes to quantum. I feel bound to hold that the Plaintiffs have failed to prove that any sum is due under this head.' (p721)

6.12   Head office overheads are usually calculated by use of a formula, although, as far as practicable, the contractor's actual loss should be established. The starting point often is:

$$\frac{\text{Overhead cost for year}}{\text{Turnover for the year}} \times 100 = \text{Percentage addition}$$

It is not surprising to find that head office costs are rarely adequately allocated to specific projects, nor is there any good reason why they should be. However, this does raise a problem when trying to determine how much of the ongoing head office cost should be allocated to the delayed project. To overcome this problem a formula is usually deployed to evaluate the proper allocation of cost. The three main formulae in use are known as Hudson's, Emden's and Eichleay's.

6.13   The Hudson and Emden formulae have both found judicial
       approval. Hudson's was used in the Canadian case, *Ellis-Don Ltd
       v Parking Authority of Toronto* (1978). Emden's was adopted in
       J.F. Finnegan Ltd, although the Official Referee believed that he
       was applying Hudson's formula. Both formulae have been widely
       accepted in arbitrations held in the United Kingdom. The Eichleay
       formula, developed in the United States courts, takes its name
       from an appeal of the same name. Its use has been criticised as
       inappropriate in *Berley Industries Inc. v City of New York* (1978).
       In that case, 87% of work had been completed by the due date for
       completion, leaving only 60,000 dollars worth of work to be done
       during a long period of delay. Applying the Eichleay formula
       would have resulted in a claim of more than 19,000 dollars for
       head office overheads. The court rejected the formula approach on
       the basis that:

       'The mathematical computations under the [formula] produce
       a figure, with at best, a chance relationship to actual damages,
       and at worst, no relationship at all.'

       If one of the above formulae could be described as being preferred
       then it would probably be Emden's, closely followed by Eichleay's.
       The weakness of the Hudson formula is its reliance on the
       percentage which the contractor has allowed for in his tender for
       general overheads. Emden's, despite its limitations, does at least
       refer to actual figures achieved by the contractor for his annual
       turnover, profit and overhead costs. Generally in regard to the use
       of formulae, although *J.F. Finnegan* was hailed by certain claims
       consultants as the judicial acceptance of the use of formulae,
       perhaps significant was the defendant employer's decision not to
       challenge the legitimacy of a formula-based approach. Only the
       particular formula used was challenged.

6.14   The Hudson formula is found in *Hudson's Building and
       Engineering Contracts* (Sweet & Maxwell, 10th Ed. 1970, p599),
       where it is shown as:

$$\frac{\text{H.O./Profit \%}}{100} \quad \text{x} \quad \frac{\text{Contract Sum x period of delay (in weeks)}}{\text{Contract Period (eg in weeks)}}$$

       This formula chooses to use, as already stated, the tender figure
       for overheads and profit.

6.15   The Emden formula is found in *Emden's Construction Law* (Volume 1, Division III, para 229). It is similar to Hudson's but uses the actual accounted overhead of the contractor as opposed to the tendered figure. It is set out in the following terms:

$$\frac{h}{100} \times \frac{c}{cp} \times pd$$

where h = the head office percentage, c = the contract sum, cp = the contract period and pd = the period of delay. cp and pd should be calculated in the same units (eg weeks).

6.16   Eichleay's formula is similar to Emden's but prefers to use the final contract price rather than the contract sum. A detailed explanation of the formulae can be found in Reg Thomas' *Construction Contract Claims* (MacMillan, 1993).

6.17   Formulae to calculate head office overheads appear in many guises but they all attempt to quantify accurately a head office loss that would be either difficult or impossible to calculate in any other way.

LOSS OF PROFIT

6.18   It is sometimes argued that a contractor has lost the opportunity to earn additional profit as a result of being delayed on another project. Perhaps he had to turn down a lucrative contract because this project continued to absorb his staff and labour. If such losses really have been incurred, then very persuasive evidence will be required before any judge or arbitrator will consider making an award. These claims are often made but rarely awarded. Claims for loss of profit generally arise as part of a common law damages claim for breach of contract and not usually as part of a contractual claim, with the possible exception of variations. Loss and expense provisions under the standard form contracts usually only relate to actual expenditure and its reimbursement.

INFLATION

6.19   Where a fixed price contract has been awarded and the contract is prolonged beyond the fixed price end date, then the contractor is usually entitled to some recompense. The value of his claim should be the excess he has had to incur as a direct result of the prolongation. He should be placed in the position he would have enjoyed had he been allowed to complete on time. Again evidence is of paramount importance. Records must be kept showing how labour and material prices were higher when the work was actually carried out compared with the prices prevailing when the work was programmed to be carried out. A common method used by claims advisors is to deduct the fixed price from the tender sum and revert to pricing the whole job on the NEDO formula or similar. This often overcompensates the claimant. In times of low inflation this head is usually less contentious.

LOSS OF PRODUCTIVITY AND ACCELERATION

6.20   This head of claim is by far the most difficult to agree, not because of difficulty in pricing, but because of a lack of clearly identifiable evidence. A wise construction lawyer once said that there were three simple rules to follow for success before any tribunal. They were: keep good records, keep good records and finally, keep good records.

6.21   A contractor is not only entitled to be reimbursed for delays but also for disturbance to the planned progress of his works. If the contractor's records clearly demonstrate that he has been financially disadvantaged because of the employer's default then he may seek reimbursement, even if the project completes on time. The planned progress of the works is usually deemed to be the agreed contract programme. The evidence advanced to support disruption claims is often presented in the form of bar charts or critical path analyses, sometimes supported by resource histograms. On occasions, the evidence provided is not explicit in that it fails to link cause with effect. Ideally the contractor should demonstrate, using an updated programme, how the disruption affected the programme and the workforce. It is important that the programme used shows the actual progress of the job rather than simply being the tender programme. An actual programme will indicate those delaying and disruptive events already having an impact on the works when the employer causes or is responsible for further disruption. This will allow the contractor to assess honestly the impact of the employer's disruption whilst ensuring that he does not claim for problems of his own making. Many claims for loss of productivity fail because good contemporaneous records do not exist and the contractor can only guess who was to blame for which loss. Other claims fail because the contractor will not acknowledge that he has been at fault in any way. Adjudicators, of any type, know that it is a rare case indeed where all of the blame lies with one party.

6.22   Another version of the loss of productivity claim is the
        acceleration claim. Few of the standard forms give the employer's
        representative the power to instruct a contractor to accelerate the
        works. When assessing a contractor's possible entitlement to
        extensions of time under JCT 80, architects should not disregard
        the fact that the contractor may impliedly have a duty to
        accelerate by reason of the wording of Clause 25 JCT 80. The
        significant clauses (with emphasis added) are Clauses 25·3·4·1 and
        25·3·4.2:

            '4·1 the Contractor shall use constantly his *best endeavours* to
            prevent delay in the progress of the Works, howsoever
            caused, ...'

            '4·2 the Contractor shall do all that may reasonably be
            required to the satisfaction of the Architect/the Contract
            Administrator to proceed with the Works'.

        The words 'best endeavours' clearly have cost implications however
        much there is a qualification in regard to expense inserted by the
        words 'may reasonably be required' in Clause 25·3·4·2. One
        exception that provides expressly for acceleration is the FIDIC form
        of contract. Clause 46 permits an employer to order a contractor
        who is in culpable delay to accelerate. Other exceptions are Clause
        11.8 of ACA Edition 2; Clause 3·6 of JCT 87; Clause 43 of
        GC/Works/1 Edition 3. In the absence of a specific contractual
        provision to cover acceleration, to ensure reimbursement under this
        head of claim the acceleration methods and associated costs must be
        agreed between the parties before the work is speeded up. If the
        financial consequences of acceleration are not agreed in advance any
        instruction to accelerate under JCT 80 or IFC 84 becomes a
        variation which is valued as such. Contractors should always bear in
        mind that if the contract has already suffered disruption, then it is
        highly probable that there will be further disruption during the
        period of acceleration. Provision needs to be made in the acceleration
        agreement for any further delays and disruption before a contractor
        can agree to evaluate the cost of acceleration. In some cases the
        acceleration proceeds without prior agreement on price. If this
        should happen then the evaluation must be based upon the factual
        evidence available after completion. The procedure for evaluating
        these losses is broadly the same as for evaluating disruption. There
        are, however, reasons why the mere process of accelerating the works
        may cause a drop in productivity. Among these are:

- Learning curve for additional operatives
- Drop in hourly production rates due to fatigue and long hours
- Congestion of working areas
- Increased pressure on supervision
- Higher proportion of defective work

A detailed study has been prepared by Professor Horner of Dundee University on the effects of accelerated completion of building works. The results show that in many cases percentage productivity losses can be supported by historical data.

6.23   An acceleration agreement is, by its very nature, an agreement to implement accelerative measures. Usually such measures are undertaken without any express guarantee that completion will be achieved earlier. The courts have examined acceleration agreements on a number of occasions and even where the outcome expected from the agreement was not fully achieved, it has been held that the client was obliged to pay (*Lester Williams v Roffey Brothers & Nicholls (Contractors) Ltd* (1990)).

FINANCING CHARGES AND INTEREST

6.24   As more fully discussed in Section 3, English law does not generally permit creditors to claim interest charges from defaulting debtors in the absence of an appropriately drafted contractual provision. Scots law incidentally does provide for recovery of interest at common law. Most standard form construction contracts fail to offer recompense for late payment. A notable exception to this are the ICE Conditions of Contract. Legislation designed to remedy this anomaly and penalise late payers is now being actively discussed and has been the subject of both EC and national government reports. Actual legislative measures are, at the time of writing, not imminent and appear to have been taken off the political agenda.

6.25   As the law stands, if a contractor wishes to pursue a claim for interest he must issue a writ or begin arbitration proceedings. The award of interest is then made at the court rate (8% simple interest at the time of writing) in High Court and County Court proceedings and in arbitration at the discretion of the arbitrator, although he would be unwise to depart from the court rate or compound interest without good cause. A judge has the power to award the interest that has accrued from the date the cause of action arose to the date of judgment. This express power is given to judges by a combination of the Law Reform (Miscellaneous Provisions) Act 1934 and the Administration of Justice Act 1982. An implied power is also given to arbitrators. Academic lawyers and commentators have pointed out that as arbitration can be commenced as soon as a payment is late, this remedy will readily permit recovery of full interest on debts.

6.26   Sub-contractors using the BEC forms, DOM/1 and 2, the NAM and NSC forms, are protected inasmuch as they can disallow main contractor's discount if they are paid outside the contractual times for payment. Whilst 2.5% is little enough, it is at least some modest contribution to cash flow.

6.27   As well as common law and statutory interest awarded as part of the damages in litigation and arbitration (discussed in Section 3) courts and arbitrators do accept that contractors survive on cash flow. A major part of the loss and expense that could be suffered by a claimant might arise from a loss of potential interest or an expenditure on overdraft interest. In many cases these 'financing charges' are allowed and are awarded as a part of the contractor's loss and expense claim.

6.28   In *F.G. Minter Ltd v Welsh Health Technical Services Organisation* (1980) it was held that interest is recoverable by a contractor under the JCT forms if it represents financing charges included in his loss and expense claim. Clause 26·1 of JCT 80 includes the words 'or is likely to incur direct loss and/or expense'. This means that a limitation in the *Minter* case (which was decided on JCT 63) has now been overcome, ie the continuing requirement to make periodic applications for loss and expense already incurred. As long as contractors notify the architect of their continuing loss and expense with regard to financing they will stand to recover their losses from the date that the base costs were incurred. It was suggested in *Rees & Kirby Ltd v Swansea City Council* (1985) that there might be no need for express reference to interest as financing charges in a written application. Common sense dictates that reference to financing charges should still be made despite the revised wording in JCT 80.

6.29   The *Minter* decision was followed by the Court of Appeal in the later case of *Rees & Kirby*, where the court held that:

• financing charges can be compounded;

- financing charges do not accrue during an intervening event, such as when a contractor suspends his application during settlement talks;
- financing charges do not apply to breaches by the architect where he fails to certify within the stipulated time.

6.30   A contractor will often include in his claim an application for interest on liquidated and ascertained damages previously, albeit wrongfully, levied. Claims consultants rely on the decision of the Northern Ireland High Court in *Department of Environment for Northern Ireland v Farrans Construction Ltd* (1982) as authority for the proposition that the employer is in breach of contract by deducting liquidated and ascertained damages in reliance on certificates which are subsequently vitiated. It is arguable that an employer who deducts liquidated and ascertained damages in accordance with Clause 24 of JCT 80, provided he does not fall foul of the notice provisions and conditions precedent to deduction, is not in breach of contract if the architect subsequently grants an extension of time under Clause 25·3·3 of JCT 80 such as to cause the operation of Clause 24·2·2 of JCT 80:

> 'If, under clause 25·3.3, the Architect/the Contract Administrator fixes a later Completion Date the Employer shall pay or repay to the Contractor any amounts recovered allowed or paid under clause 24·2·1, for the period up to such later Completion Date.'

Any employer or his architect considering a contractor's claim for interest following the repayment of liquidated and ascertained damages under JCT 80 should point to the strict wording of Clause 24·2·2 as a defence. What appears to be stipulated is a contractual repayment without any right to interest.

CLAIM PREPARATION COSTS
6.31   As a general rule the contractor's staff will prepare the claim as the work proceeds and the preparation costs will be recovered in the preliminaries or overheads. Where the work is done in a period of prolongation, the costs are recovered under the same heads in the prolongation claim. However, there are cases where, despite the best efforts of the contractor to evidence his loss and expense, the client's representatives fail to carry out their obligation under the contract to ascertain the losses. In these circumstances, if the contractor is put to a cost which is unreasonable and is not

otherwise recoverable he may wish to seek reimbursement on the grounds of the failure of the client's representatives. Architects should ensure that the employer's quantity surveyor is being reasonable in his ascertainment and is not placing a burden of proof on the contractor which is not demanded by the contract or the law. Some inexperienced, or perhaps cynical, quantity surveyors seem to believe or suggest that a contractor must prove his case 'beyond reasonable doubt'. This erroneous view may result in the employer bearing unnecessary legal costs when the courts find for the contractor who has properly demonstrated his entitlement on the 'balance of probabilities'.

6.32   A further problem arises when outside claim specialists are employed to prepare a claim. In these cases the principles remain the same; their costs will only be recoverable if the employer's representatives have failed in their duty properly to ascertain the loss and expense and the outside consultant has been employed to do the work instead. Generally, however, the costs of claims specialists are not recoverable unless they are acting in relation to case preparation and presentation in arbitration or are instructed to act as expert witnesses in either litigation or arbitration.

6.33   For information about what the Royal Institution of Chartered Surveyors believes is acceptable in a direct loss and expense claim, the *Quantity Surveyors Practice Pamphlet No. 7* is recommended.

6.34   Loss and expense claims are difficult to evaluate. There is never any substitute for good record-keeping and an understanding of the legal and contractual principles underlying them. Realism and honesty will make claims more readily acceptable and so enable the client to settle them more quickly. In addition, any claim must be presented in a manner which is readable and concise. How this can be achieved is explained in the next Section.

7 Presenting and negotiating loss and expense claims

The written claim

7.01   The introduction of adjudication into certain standard form and other widely used construction contracts and the publication of the JCT Arbitration Rules 1988 have coincided with the new emphasis on attempts to keep costs down in arbitration and litigation. There are moves, supported by the judiciary, towards making more use of documentary evidence in place of lengthy oral presentations. In many cases barristers are now expected to submit either a skeleton argument or full opening statement in writing for the judge or arbitrator to read before the hearing. Written witness statements are also exchanged by the parties and provided to the judge or arbitrator in advance of the hearing with the documents referred to in the body of the statement appended. This practice, long adopted in arbitration, has extended to the County and High Courts. The purpose of these procedural changes and others in regard to expert witnesses is that time-consuming evidence in chief can be reduced to a minimum and the traditional recourse to 'trial by ambush' avoided. Although arbitration conducted by documents alone will only ever be possible in the least complex cases, the number of matters dealt with in this way is growing. A simpler and better prepared approach does help to keep court costs down by reducing the length of hearings. Associated costs, such as the costs of legal representation and experts, are similarly reduced.

7.02   At a conference on arbitration law an eminent retired judge commented that he had never encountered a construction case that could not be summarised on four sides of A4 paper. Experience had presumably taught him that some of the people involved in the litigation process were more long-winded than was necessary. There are three techniques that can assist in the presentation of claims which will satisfy not only the needs of the case but also find favour with those considering the merits of a claim whether they be judge, arbitrator, architect or quantity surveyor. They are:

• high quality of presentation;
• conciseness and clarity;
• properly evidenced arguments and contentions.

The same virtues should more favourably dispose an architect or quantity surveyor to the acceptance of the contractor's claim. However, although presentational techniques are important and form part of the art of persuasion, it is essential not to be blinded to the imperfections and incoherence of a claim by the impression it creates when taken at face value.

PRESENTATION

7.03   With the advent of desktop publishing and the variety of fonts available in word processing, it is now possible to produce documents of a quality that was never within the grasp of the typist with the traditional typewriter. By means of additional computer software, such as spreadsheets and graphics packages, construction professionals can now produce, at their desks, very complex compilations of information and artwork which formerly would have taken many weeks to prepare as professionally. As a result even the smaller contractor has the ability to produce a document that not only reads well but also includes supporting charts, graphs, diagrams and photographs. 'A picture paints a thousand words' may be a cliché, but in the context of good claims preparation illustrative material can convey to a judge or arbitrator a complex point more clearly than a long prose narrative. For example, computer graphics are commonly used to re-create projects to display the features of delay and disruption to the anticipated programme.

7.04   Every claim should have a title page and a contents page and be bound in such a way that the pages lie flat on the reader's desk for easy reference. The claim should be broken down into sections which identify the substance of the case. The headings should be presented with their appropriate page number in the contents section. In the event that a claim does ultimately go to arbitration or litigation, barristers and judges prefer to have each paragraph numbered with a unique reference to allow rapid identification at the hearing.

7.05   Colour might be used to help make the document look more attractive. For easy reference, charts, graphs and tables are best sited in the text at the points they are most relevant rather than as appendix material. A user-friendly document will have a built-in advantage if the opponent's response is clearly less impressive and more cumbersome.

7.06   Many barristers and judges deal with construction cases regularly but are not always able to visualise the problems that have occurred on a site, and even a technical arbitrator may be unsure when new techniques, materials or methods are used in the construction. To assist non-construction professionals to understand the problems that have arisen, the claim should include good quality colour photographs. A high quality presentation is not only a boon to any contractor's case and a great help to the claims assessor but it may also be a good advertisement for the claimant's company.

7.07   Claims documents should preferably be brief, setting out the case fully and clearly in the minimum number of words. The modern tendency of subjecting the claims assessor, judge or arbitrator to a deluge of photocopied documents is to be deplored. A poor case is not enhanced by the creation of more and more sheets of paper. Judges and arbitrators have the same limitations on their attention span as everyone else, and when confronted with a claim that runs to three full lever-arch files they will be tempted to skim through the text to find the parts they consider important and may as a result miss some essential point. By keeping the presentation documents to a few pages, properly numbered and punctuated and supported by charts and diagrams, a contractor or his claims advisor will encourage the reader to consider the document in its entirety, instead of homing in on those parts which appear most interesting. Conversely, by presenting a document that is neither concise nor clear, the contractor or his claims consultant risks not only alienating the adjudicator but also doing a disservice to a good claim.

7.08   It is important to use plain English and avoid, as far as possible, jargon and specialist terminology. Technical words should be explained in full. The aim is to convey the strengths of the contractor's case to the claims assessor and through him the client as clearly as possible. An excellent test of a document's effectiveness is to invite a complete outsider to review it, comment on its presentation and content, and act as 'devil's advocate'. The different emphases that individuals will place on the same written document can be surprising. The contractor's intention must be to ensure that everyone who reads his document will draw only one conclusion: the same conclusion which the architect or quantity surveyor will draw.

CONCISENESS AND CLARITY

7.09   Although good presentation and a clear and precise text will
ensure the best possible start to the process of claims resolution,
these aspects are less important than the content of the claim itself
which must support the case and convince the reader of its merits.
It is up to the claimant to provide clear evidence in a form which
is ultimately acceptable to any adjudicating tribunal. The claim
document must contain:

   - the particulars of the parties involved in the dispute;
   - the role of the parties in the dispute;
   - the name and details of the originator of the document;
   - an explanation of the dispute, including any relevant
     contractual details;
   - a statement of events, particularly those which gave rise to the
     dispute;
   - the effect of any breaches on the claimant's work or
     performance;
   - an explanation of how the claimant's performance was hindered
     by the breach;
   - how the costs incurred relate to the breach;
   - full quantification of the damage incurred;
   - a conclusion stating the sums of monies claimed.

7.10   Case law, including *Wharf Properties Ltd and Another v Eric
Cumine Associates (No.2)* (1991) and *ICI Plc v Bovis Construction
Ltd and Others* (1992), indicates that if the case is not pleaded with
full particularity, showing cause and effect, the courts may
consider it an abuse of the process and strike the case out either in
its entirety or in part. For this reason it is advisable to avoid
speculative claims formatted as vague rolled-up or global claims.

7.11   The claimant himself is usually responsible for drafting or
employing a claims consultant to prepare the original claim
document, which may then be used by counsel to plead the case if
formal proceedings in litigation or arbitration become necessary
following a failure to negotiate an adequate settlement. It is almost
certain that any inaccuracies or untruths included in the original
claim document, particularly exaggerated figures put forward as
the contractor's losses, will appear in the pleadings too. For this
reason contractors and all claims consultants should remember
that a claim document drafted for the purpose of negotiation only
is unlikely to be suitable for litigation or arbitration. Prior to

submitting the claim document to counsel for him to plead upon, the writer would be well advised to review his document to ensure that every statement, fact and figure can be substantiated by witnesses of fact or by reference to documents. Particular attention should be paid to the quantification of alleged losses.

7.12   Mention of witnesses of fact leads to the matter of witness statements and their preparation. Ultimately an unresolved claim will rely on people – quantity surveyor, site agent, estimator, etc – to prove its legitimacy by personal recollection before a judge or arbitrator. Much of the guidance concerning claims preparation also applies to witness statements. These should be clear, concise and in the language of the person who is giving the statement. The witness may have to undergo cross-examination on his statement at some future trial or arbitration hearing. It is very important that the statement reflects his true opinion, otherwise, unless he is an expert liar, he will be discredited by a persistent cross-examination from the other party's counsel. It is in everyone's interests to ensure that there is the same level of accuracy in the witness statements as in the claim document. To pursue or defend a case on the basis of falsehood will cause costs to escalate unnecessarily for everyone. If the claimant's case fails, he may bear the burden not only of his lost claim but also his costs and the costs of the other party. The respondent can find himself in a similar position. Too many claims are prosecuted or defended that choose to ignore the underlying reality of the facts until it is too late to avoid high costs to lawyer and expert witness.

EVIDENCE AND ARGUMENT

7.13   As well as being clear, concise and well prepared, the claim document should be honest and cogent so that the architect or quantity surveyor who receives it will be prompted to discuss terms of settlement. That said, undue credence should not be given to a well presented but poorly evidenced claim. When a four-volume claim arrives liberally laced with charts, formulae, graphs and a mass of calculations, it is easy to assume that because so many documents are being presented, there must be some substance in the case. The question that claims assessors need to ask is, how much hard evidence is there to support the arguments of the claimant?

7.14   Paragraph 7.09 listed what should be in a claim, but to what extent should the claimant set out to prove or substantiate his allegations? In theory, no claim should survive if evidence is unavailable, but in practice many do and are paid because they give the appearance of solidity and legal entitlement. Claims assessors need to ensure that on the balance of probabilities the claim is allowable in the sum claimed.

7.15   Evidence can be actual, suggested or simply absent from an apparently well presented claim. Actual evidence is provided in contemporary documentation and includes letters, drawings, specifications and instructions. It will also arise from the records of conversations and from data relating to formal and informal meetings.

7.16   Suggested evidence can be presented in the form of charts, histograms and graphs that demonstrate how things probably happened. If the charts are based upon actual evidence then they become actual evidence themselves. If they are extrapolations from actual data then they become suggested evidence. Should a chart present information not available to all parties at the time – an example might be tendered hours – then it should be treated cautiously, as it may not be evidence at all. Formulae are one of the best known methods of presenting suggested evidence. By using historical data or researched criteria it is possible to demonstrate that the outcome could have been A (but it is important not to lose sight of the fact that the outcome could equally well have been B). The better the underlying records the greater the value of the interpolated, extrapolated or calculated result.

7.17   It is not unknown for claimants to create the illusion of evidence where in reality no evidence exists. There are two common methods of achieving this:

  • Constant repetition. If something is said enough times it must be true.
  • Bulk. A thick volume suggests great depth and research.

Assessors should always look behind the facade and examine the foundations on which the claim is built. Statements should not be accepted as facts: they should be questioned and examined in detail. Architects may find that the claim is absolutely correct and further monies are due to the contractor, but the time has still been well spent if monies can be certified with a clear conscience, in the confidence that a professional job has been done.

7.18   Some tactics to watch out for are:

- The extrapolation of researched data beyond the bounds recommended by the researchers, or beyond that which makes reasonable sense.
- Concentration on one particular aspect of the claim, perhaps the reasons for a particular delay, whilst other equally important aspects are glossed over. This usually suggests weakness or a lack of evidence.
- Reliance on information that is not in the public domain. This may include a contractor's job costing information, internal programmes and so forth.

Theories parading as facts or evidence abound in the claims arena. It is essential to evaluate properly the substantiating documentation to ensure that it is reasonable evidence for the case put forward.

7.19   It is unlikely that even the most unmeritorious claim will be successfully rebutted by a simple refusal to pay. Some negotiation will be necessary. The way in which both parties approach the negotiation will, in large part, determine how much of the claim is paid.

Negotiation

7.20   One definition of negotiation is that it is a process by which opposing views can be overcome, avoided or compromised. A negotiation is the coming together of two or more parties, who hold conflicting views, for the purpose of reaching agreement. The real aim is to achieve a harmonious settlement and not to disenchant the opponent or pursue personal egotistical objectives. There is more to negotiation than either simple bargaining or compromise, yet many claims for loss and expense are approached in these simplistic ways. Compromise tends to favour the stronger or more determined party and should be avoided.

7.21   Why negotiate at all, it might be asked. After all, the contracts do not contemplate a negotiated outcome. The simple answer is that the contracts define in general terms the rights and obligations of the parties and provide the mechanism to obtain legal remedies; they impose no obligation to negotiate. Only a rich or foolish person will ignore negotiation and launch straight into arbitration or litigation.

7.22   There are a number of reasons why parties should consider negotiating:

- someone may be in the wrong, and wrongdoers pay heavily in court or arbitration;
- it may be necessary to maintain good relationships for the future;
- the necessary manpower to support litigation or arbitration may be lacking;
- insufficient money may be available to finance litigation or arbitration;
- there may be a delay in matters getting to trial or final hearing.

A properly constructed and managed negotiation can give better results in a fraction of the time it takes to litigate or arbitrate. It can also be done for a fraction of the cost.

7.23   If negotiation is such a viable approach, how should it be properly conducted? A fourfold plan of action is the answer: prepare, understand, negotiate and agree. The first two actions should be undertaken before meeting the other side, and the latter two should be handled amicably in discussions.

7.24   Preparing to negotiate a loss and expense claim requires a great deal of research. It will be necessary to identify the real issues behind the claim, as these are not always stated, and to check the claim arithmetically and evidentially. Every area of weakness should be assessed and evaluated. Consideration should be given to how the other side will respond to comments from the claims assessor so as to have a reply ready. Architects should understand the contractor's case as well as the client's argument in rebuttal. In negotiation, knowledge is power.

7.25   Understanding the case that is presented by the contractor and how to respond is absolutely essential. The claims assessor should look at all of the documents and charts, understand the logic and the correlation between documents and arguments. If he has a query on a chart or a formula, he should contact the contractor and ask for an explanation. Any failure to understand the documents or follow the contractor's reasoning does not place the claims assessor at fault: it is more likely that the fault lies with the contractor in putting across his case. Contractors or claims assessors should be clear about what they want from the negotiation. It may be practicable to have a 'dry run' to iron out any disagreements within the negotiating team. It is essential to present a united, confident and well prepared team to the other party.

7.26   Having researched and understood the claim the architect or quantity surveyor should be ready to negotiate. The purpose of the negotiation is to find the right solution to the problem, not to remain restricted to a predetermined ideal. Be ready to listen, concede valid points and make financial allowances if appropriate. It is to be hoped that somewhere between the parties' expectations will be a margin for agreement. Whether it is closer to one side's expectations or the other's is irrelevant, as long as the right price is paid for the work done. The parties to a negotiation should explain their case in a clear and reasoned way, giving the other side an opportunity to point out any errors or misconceptions.

7.27   Tactical negotiation is prevalent in the construction industry with parties sometimes resorting to coercion, blackmail and threats. If such tactics are used, the party subjected to them should make it clear that he cannot be influenced by disreputable behaviour of this kind and that he can only to be persuaded by cogent argument.

7.28   Not all negotiations have a negotiating margin and one side may have to give way. When this is the case it should be achieved by concession and counter-concession so that one side does not feel damaged or abused. Bad deals seldom stick and can often turn into vitriolic litigation. If agreement is to be reached then it should be by proposal and counter-proposal, brainstorming or, only as a last resort, compromise.

7.29   The proposal/counter-proposal method is commonplace in loss and expense negotiations. A contractor will submit his claim and provide his reasoning. The client side will point out errors in the reasoning, the arithmetic or the perceived legal basis to the claim. The contractor will consider these points, allow for them and resubmit his case. After a series of such interchanges the gaps are narrowed to a point where agreement is possible. This is probably the most appropriate method for negotiating claims.

7.30   Occasionally, there seems to be no scope for reaching agreement because the parties are too far apart. This is often because they have taken up entrenched positions. A golden rule for success is to negotiate outcomes, not positions. There are two reasons. First, neither party has to climb down from a stated position; second,

most commercial parties should really be interested in the outcome
and not in defeating the other side. After all, these are mere
skirmishes, not battles.

7.31   It may seem strange that compromise is not recommended as a
method of reaching agreement, but this is a matter of
understanding the underlying psychology. With compromise,
neither side really knows what was achievable, and once the
euphoria of settlement has ebbed away, a grumbling dissatisfaction
often remains. Did they get the best deal possible, did they leave
money on the table, were they deceived? These niggling doubts are
less likely to persist when agreement has been reached by a more
investigative approach.

7.32   Once agreement is reached, the parties should record it in writing
as soon as possible. This prevents backsliding and helps those with
selective memories to remember both the good and bad points of
the agreement. A written agreement of this nature will also be
good evidence should a dispute arise later.

7.33   There will always be a time when good preparation is simply not
enough to avoid a heated dispute, and in these cases it may be
advisable to bring in a third party neutral to mediate the dispute
or carry out one of the other alternative dispute resolution (ADR)
processes. The role a third party neutral can fulfil is discussed in
Section 8 along with the traditional methods of dispute resolution,
arbitration and litigation.

8   Dispute resolution

Arbitration

8.01   Most construction contracts, including all those of the JCT family,
anticipate that dispute resolution will primarily be by means of
arbitration. Over recent years the problems of arbitration have
been much debated. Certain construction professionals believe that
arbitration has been hijacked by lawyers and turned into
something akin to the litigation process in the High Court. Such
people remember, or choose to remember, an earlier period when
arbitration was a cheap and quick method of dispute resolution
shorn of much of the paraphernalia of the legal process. By and
large the comment of Sir John Donaldson MR in *Northern
Regional Health Authority v Derek Crouch Construction Co Ltd*
(1984) that arbitration is 'usually no more and no less than
litigation in the private sector' well describes the present situation.

8.02   The obvious question is, can arbitration ever be really different
from litigation? There is a danger that the present clamour for a
'back to basics' approach is, although well intentioned, an exercise
in unreality. Arbitration, like litigation, is essentially designed to
identify and establish the legal rights and obligations of the
parties; it is not some form of alternative dispute resolution.
Construction disputes are usually complex, not least those relating
to loss and expense claims. Apart from applying the law correctly
to a given set of facts, an arbitrator, no less than a judge, needs to
examine facts that interrelate and combine, where causation needs
to be demonstrated and proved. A common but frequently difficult
problem that arises in the analysis of construction disputes is the
effect of concurrent delays, not all of which will necessarily be the
employer's responsibility. Because construction disputes are
complex, they rely heavily on witnesses of fact appearing before a
judge or arbitrator and having their recollections and suppositions
subjected to cross-examination. Too many claims in the
construction industry commence on the basis that a project was
programmed to complete in x weeks, only to be completed in y
weeks. The contract value was £x, whereas the 'as built' costs were
£y. The contractor starts from the glib proposition that he is
entitled to the difference between the contract value and the 'as
built' cost as his direct loss and/or expense. However much
additional documentation is provided by claims consultants, many

claims are, beneath the reams of paper, little more than global in their composition. Proper analysis of such claims in the adversarial climate which arbitration shares with litigation is inevitably time-consuming and expensive. For this reason parties who commence an arbitration thinking it is more cost-effective than litigation may end up with a hearing of several weeks' duration or more and a costs bill of several hundred thousand pounds. (An apposite example was the claim for £20,000 which went to final hearing before a well known construction arbitrator with a total costs bill of £250,000.) Further, construction professionals should not forget that arbitration law and practice have long been part of the legal process. Since 1697 arbitration in England and Wales has been subject to legislative control. The present control is found in the Arbitration Acts 1950, 1975 and 1979. A new consolidating statute to replace these three Acts has now been drafted as a consultative Bill. When passed, the new legislation will not remove arbitration from the legal process, and the draft Bill has already been criticised for retaining what are perceived by many as the outmoded and legalistic principles of the present legislation. In addition to direct legislative control over arbitration, the process is further subject to a plethora of case law decisions, many of which are complex and contradictory in their application.

8.03   Apart from the JCT Arbitration Rules 1988, which are commented on in paragraphs 8.05–9, many other changes which would streamline arbitration procedure have been recognised by lawyers and claims consultants as sound in principle, even though such modifications are sometimes little used in the conduct of specific arbitration hearings. Perhaps surprisingly, many procedural short cuts, now common to litigation and arbitration, were in fact pioneered by the Official Referees in the High Court. These include exchange of expert witness reports, meetings of experts to agree 'figures as figures' and generally to identify those issues in the dispute that can be agreed and not agreed, and the exchange of statements by witnesses of fact. Further modifications made by most arbitrators include dispensing with opening and closing speeches other than in a written format, and allowing the witness statements of the lay witnesses to stand as evidence in chief. In addition, some arbitrators limit the time available to the parties to present their case. However, whatever legitimate methods are adopted to limit the length of hearings, the need to test the evidence of the other party by detailed cross-examination can never be dispensed with, and this is probably the most time-consuming aspect of any trial or arbitration hearing.

8.04   Attempts to speed up the arbitration process usually seem to fail. Counsel and expert witnesses, whose business is the process of litigation, are often unavailable to commence a hearing on a particular date, although they have considerable advance warning of the time commitments. Further, whether a case proceeds by way of conventional pleadings, as understood by lawyers, or by way of apparently fuller statements of case with all supporting documentation included in the statement of case, the lawyers' and claims consultants' desire for further information by way of further and better particulars never appears to be fully satisfied. In all litigation, including arbitration, requests for further and better particulars (and replies to them), frequently difficult to resist, often delay the process of bringing the matter to trial or final hearing.

THE JCT ARBITRATION RULES 1988
8.05   Concerned at the reputation arbitration was getting in the late 1980s for being slow and expensive, and for its over-legalistic approach, the JCT introduced new Arbitration Rules, discussed below in paragraphs 8.06–9, to allow greater flexibility in arbitrations arising under the JCT contracts.

8.06   The JCT Arbitration Rules 1988 envisage a dispute being settled in one of three ways:

   • by written statements only without a hearing (a Rule 5 arbitration);
   • by written statements plus a hearing (a Rule 6 arbitration);
   • by a short procedure plus a hearing (a Rule 7 arbitration).

8.07   It is open to the parties to decide which procedure to follow. If they cannot decide, the dispute will be settled under Rule 5 unless the arbitrator is persuaded that use of Rule 6 would be more appropriate. If the claimant wants a Rule 7 arbitration, he must formulate his case in sufficient detail to persuade the respondent to agree to a hearing under this Rule. If the respondent is not so persuaded then the arbitrator must choose between a Rule 5 or a Rule 6 arbitration. The arbitrator cannot require a Rule 7 arbitration. Similarly, a claimant requires the consent of the respondent before there can be a Rule 7 arbitration.

8.08   Although flexibility is built into the JCT Rules, the appropriateness of a documents-only arbitration (a Rule 5 arbitration) may be limited to situations where the correspondence is self-explanatory, comprehensive and factually non-contentious and matters of contract interpretation are at issue. This would appear to rule out its application in almost all construction disputes, including loss and expense claims. It is further open to question whether an arbitrator may be criticised for not requiring a hearing under Rule 6 when one party only is in favour of a documents-only hearing under Rule 5.

8.09   It is said that the great advantage of the JCT Rules is that they ensure a speedy outcome to arbitrations. Slowness and cost, as previously stated, are often taken to be the two most negative hallmarks of arbitration. Provided that the relevant Rules are complied with, the period for concluding an arbitration varies from 112 days for a Rule 5 arbitration, to 154 days plus the period to and length of the hearing for a Rule 6 arbitration, and 49 days for a Rule 7 arbitration. If a statement is not served by the due date for a Rule 5 or a Rule 6 arbitration, the arbitrator is required to give the defaulting party formal notice that he has a further 7 days in which to comply. If he does not, the arbitrator may proceed without him. A claimant who fails to serve a statement of case on time can find the arbitrator dismissing the claim and ordering the claimant to pay the fees and expenses of the arbitrator and any costs incurred by the respondent. Moreover, if the defaulting party's statement is delivered late, the arbitrator is required to disregard it unless the defaulting party can give a good and proper reason why the statement was not served by him on time and why a request for an extension of time was not properly made. In this regard an extension of time will only be given if the arbitrator is satisfied that the need for it arose on account of a matter which could reasonably be considered to be outside the control of the party concerned. The Rules, which require service of the various pleadings within 14 days for a Rule 5 arbitration and 28 days for a Rule 6 arbitration, are somewhat loaded against an employer who receives a loss and expense claim from a contractor many months after the works are completed. In truth, the JCT Rules time periods are too short to investigate claims and formulate responses in detail, particularly where an employer's in-house personnel and outside advisers need to be interviewed. The advice of many lawyers to employers is to discard the JCT Rules completely.

8.10   Second, the pleadings of the party should be:

- comprehensive documents setting out the nature of the case being made;
- the facts relied upon; and
- the legal basis of the claim or counterclaim.

The JCT Rules further require a party serving a particular pleading to list those documents which are considered necessary to support its case (in the case of a Rule 5 or Rule 6 arbitration) together with a copy of the relevant documents with the necessary passages highlighted. The JCT Rules are also designed to reduce discovery and inspection (again an expensive process in traditional arbitration and litigation) although the arbitrator has a residual power (Rule 12.1.7) to require a party to give further and better discovery.

JCT 80

8.11   As far as dispute resolution under JCT 80 is concerned, Article 5 of the Articles of Agreement provides that disputes will be settled by arbitration:

'A5 If any dispute or difference as to the construction of this contract or any matter or thing of whatsoever nature shall arise between the Employer or the Architect on his behalf and the Contractor either during the progress or after completion or abandonment of the Works ... it shall be and is hereby referred to arbitration in accordance with Clause 41.' (JCT Amendment 4: 1987).

8.12   The matters to be referred to arbitration include any dispute between the employer and the contractor in regard to the latter's entitlement to direct loss and/or expense. Clause 41 requires written notice from the party initiating the reference to arbitration and states the procedures for appointing an arbitrator. Unless the parties agree otherwise, arbitration will usually not take place until after practical completion has been achieved or work ceased (Clause 41·3). Although there are a number of exceptions to this principle, these do not extend to early resolution of a contractor's entitlement to direct loss and/or expense. By Clause 41·4, the arbitrator is given powers which include the right to 'review and revise any certificate, opinion or decision of the Architect'. This right of review empowers the arbitrator to review and revise any

assessment made by the architect or the quantity surveyor acting
on behalf of the architect.

8.13   Subject to a party's right of appeal to the High Court on points of
law, by agreement or with leave of the court, an arbitrator's award
(which can be registered as a judgment of the High Court under
s26 Arbitration Act 1950 for the purpose of enforcement) is
ordinarily final and binding on the parties. On occasions, the right
of appeal to the High Court, provided by s1(2) Arbitration Act
1950, is excluded by the parties by agreement in accordance with
s3(1) Arbitration Act 1979. Under Clause 41·6 of JCT 80 the
parties, by agreement or with leave of the Court, specifically retain
the right of appeal to the High Court on matters of law. Unless
deleted, since JCT Amendment 6: 1988, the JCT Arbitration Rules
1988 have applied to all arbitrations on JCT 80 contracts.

8.14   The presence of an arbitration clause, at least in the form drafted,
has produced some surprising consequences under JCT 80. The
courts have consistently held they have in general no powers 'to
open up review and revise any certificate, opinion, decision,
requirement or notice' of the architect under JCT 80. The court's
lack of power to re-examine certificates, opinions and decisions of
the architect would obviously extend to any subsequent re-
assessment of an architect's previous ascertainment of a
contractor's entitlement to direct loss and/or expense. This
principle was established in *Northern Regional Health Authority v
Derek Crouch Construction Co Ltd* (1984). The problem created by
this case may now be of less practical significance. Section 100 of
the Courts and Legal Services Act 1990 inserts a new s43A in the
Supreme Court Act 1981. With the consent of the parties, the
courts are now empowered to deal with disputes previously caught
by *Derek Crouch*. Further, in certain cases the courts have
successfully side-stepped the *Derek Crouch* decision. For instance,
this occurred in *J.F. Finnegan Ltd v Sheffield City Council* (1988).
In that case the Official Referee concluded that because the
contractual mechanism to assess and award the contractor's direct
loss and expense had broken down, he was empowered to hear a
dispute about direct loss and expense under an amended JCT 80
form.

IFC 84

8.15   The arbitration provisions in IFC 84 operate in a similar way to
those under JCT 80. By Clause 9·8 of IFC 84 arbitrations are

subject to the JCT Arbitration Rules 1988 'current at the Base Date'. This is stated in the Appendix to the IFC 84 Conditions, although the parties may by written notice to the arbitrator agree the adoption of later or amended rules.

8.16 The procedure for appointing the arbitrator is set out in Clause 9·1. Either the employer or contractor will serve on the other a written notice seeking concurrence in the appointment of an arbitrator, with the facility to apply to the appointing body named in the Appendix in the event of a failure to agree the appointment within 14 days of the written notice. By Clause 9·3 the arbitrator's powers include powers 'to ascertain and award any sum which ought to have been the subject of or included in any certificate and to open up, review and revise any certificate, opinion, decision, requirement ...' [of the architect or contract administrator]. Such wording means that the difficulties caused by *Derek Crouch* may also affect IFC 84 arbitrations.

MW 80

8.17 The position under MW 80 needs to be discussed separately. The contract calls for the resolution of disputes by arbitration and, unless Clause 9·5 is deleted, the JCT Arbitration Rules current at the date of contract apply. The appointment of an arbitrator is dealt with generally in Article 4 and Clause 9. MW 80 can be distinguished from JCT 80 and IFC 84 in that arbitration is possible during the currency of the works. 'Any dispute or difference as to the construction of this Agreement or any matter or thing of whatsoever nature arising thereunder or in connection therewith can be referred to an agreed arbitrator, or, in the event of a failure to agree within 14 days of the date of the written request to agree, to an arbitrator nominated by the party named in Article 4.'

8.18 The *Derek Crouch* principle does not now appear to have any relevance to MW 80 arbitrations. The power of the courts to open up, review and revise certificates, opinions and decisions of the architect under MW 80 has been discussed in a number of cases. The decision in *Oram Builders Ltd v M.J. Pemberton and Another* (1984), where the judge chose to follow *Derek Crouch*, conflicts with those in *Benstrete Construction Ltd v Angus Hill* (1987) and *Chrisphine Othieno v Mr. and Mrs. Cooper* (1991). It is now fairly well established that under MW 80 an arbitrator does not have the same exclusive jurisdiction as under JCT 80 and IFC 84, and such matters as valuations, including loss and expense, can be reviewed by the courts.

GC/WORKS/1

8.19   Under GC/Works/1 Edition 3, 'differences or questions between the Authority and the Contractor arising out of or relating to the Contract, other than a matter as to which a decision is expressed to be final and conclusive' (Clause 60(1)) are referred to a single agreed arbitrator, or, in default of agreement within a reasonable period, to one appointed by the Chartered Institute of Arbitrators. Significantly, the Authority, as defined in the contract, will request the appointment. A strict framework, set by Clause 60(2), attempts to address some of the criticisms of arbitration. It establishes:

(a) no reference can be made to arbitration until after completion, alleged completion, abandonment of the works or determination of the contract;
(b) the arbitrator will hold a preliminary meeting with the parties to fix a timetable for exchange of pleadings, discovery and inspection of documents, and arrangements for a hearing. Importantly, the timetable will not, without the consent of the parties, exceed six months from the date of the preliminary meeting;
(c) the parties will ensure that all matters to be submitted to the arbitrator are submitted in accordance with the agreed timetable. The arbitrator will make his award within three months of the period mentioned in (b).

8.20   On occasions, one of the parties will commence proceedings in the High Court or the County Court notwithstanding the presence in the standard form contracts of an arbitration clause. An example might be where the contractor knows that the architect or quantity surveyor has ascertained direct loss and/or expense in a specific amount and there has been a delay in the release of those monies to the contractor. The existence of an arbitration clause in a contract is a reflection of the parties' agreement to settle all their disputes or differences by arbitration, and there is a presumption in favour of obliging them to resolve any disputes or differences by this method. Therefore, s4(1) of the Arbitration Act 1950 permits a party against whom court proceedings are commenced to seek a stay of those proceedings pending a reference to arbitration.

8.21   Even if party B intends to seek a stay of proceedings served on
        him by party A to arbitration he must nevertheless acknowledge
        service of any writ in order to prevent party A obtaining judgment
        in default. Party B must then immediately seek a stay of the
        proceedings to arbitration by sending to the relevant court a
        summons (asking for the proceedings to be stayed to arbitration)
        together with a supporting affidavit which sets out the reasons
        why the matter should be dealt with in arbitration. Usually the
        defendant will do little more than point to the fact that the
        contract is a standard form which contains an arbitration clause.
        It is important that party B does not do anything that might be
        seen as a waiver of the arbitration agreement. Acts of waiver
        would include service of a Defence in the High Court or a formal
        request to the court for more time to serve a Defence. An informal
        request by party B to party A for more time to serve a Defence
        does not nullify party B's rights to seek a transfer of the
        proceedings to arbitration (*Brighton Marine Palace and Pier
        Limited v Woodhouse* (1893)).

8.22   Although the presumption is in favour of transferring proceedings
        to arbitration whenever there is a written arbitration clause, there
        are a number of circumstances when the courts will not do this.
        These include:

        • when the relief sought by party A is outside the arbitration
          agreement. This is a technical matter for lawyers. On occasions,
          an arbitration clause is drafted in terms that an arbitrator
          cannot deal with such issues as equitable remedies and
          negligence;

        • when arbitration would cause unnecessary expense or
          inconsistent decisions in that there is potential multi-party
          litigation. An obvious example would be in the case of a
          defective building where there is the possibility of a myriad of
          claims against contractor, architect, engineer, materials'
          suppliers, etc;

        • when the issues raised on the facts of a particular case are
          essentially matters of law. The problem with arbitration is that
          it cannot create benchmarks for application in subsequent cases
          in which the same point is at issue. For instance, although
          many arbitrations had considered the question of a contractor's
          right to extensions of time under JCT 80 for events occurring

during a period of culpable overrun, it was not until the decision of the High Court in *Balfour Beatty Building Ltd v Chestermount Properties Ltd* (1993) that there was a definitive judgment from the courts which could be applied in other similar cases.

8.23   In cases where the contractor has not received certified monies when expected (which could include direct loss and/or expense previously ascertained) he is often advised by his lawyer to seek summary judgment. This is sometimes also known as Order 14 because of the particular Rule of the Supreme Court under which the High Court can give judgment in a plaintiff's favour without a full trial. The plaintiff sets out his case in the form of an affidavit and makes his application on the basis that the defendant has no arguable defence to the claim. However, case law has demonstrated that the mere issue of an architect's certificate is no bar to cross claims being raised on behalf of the employer. Therefore, it is open to an employer on a contractor's application to the High Court for payment of sums certified to raise all manner of cross claims.

8.24   Ordinarily when a contractor makes an application to the High Court for summary judgment this will be met by a cross application from the employer to transfer the proceedings to arbitration. Clearly such a manoeuvre is to the advantage of the employer because arbitration does not have, as a general principle, any process akin to summary judgment in the High Court.

8.25   The immediate problem faced by the court is to decide which summons should be heard first. In *Ellis Mechanical Services Ltd v Wates Construction Ltd* (1976) the court was of the opinion that it was appropriate to hear the summary judgment application first. If it could be adequately resolved that the defendant had no arguable defence to the plaintiff's claim there was clearly no claim to refer to arbitration. Unfortunately an element of confusion was subsequently created by the decision of the Commercial Court in the non-construction law case, *Hayter v Nelson and Home Insurance Co* (1990), where the judge took the view that as soon as the summary judgment application was disputed there was a dispute or difference within the meaning of the arbitration clause, even if the particular dispute was capable of easy resolution. Therefore the judge felt obliged to transfer proceedings to arbitration. That said, to a large extent the decision in *Hayter* can be seen as 'maverick', and the general pattern will remain that in construction cases a court will always look at the merits of a summary judgment application before considering a defendant's application to transfer the proceedings to arbitration.

Alternative dispute resolution

8.26   The general sense of dissatisfaction with both litigation and arbitration has led to demands for a better method of dispute resolution. This has largely been responsible for the growth of alternative dispute resolution (ADR), which is becoming an increasingly prominent feature of English dispute resolution following its birth and initial growth in the United States. ADR attempts to bring together parties who at first sight have no common interests. Rather than concentrate on the establishment of rights, as does the legal process or arbitration, it seeks to achieve operable solutions between the parties. It recognises that many disputes occur because a particular individual within an organisation has a position to protect, has made a mistake and is unwilling to admit his error. It also recognises that neither litigation nor arbitration necessarily provides any 'lever' on a defendant or respondent to promote a quicker negotiated settlement. Frequently what litigation or arbitration achieves is that the parties become more and more entrenched until the dispute is resolved by way of a belated 'horse-trade', by which time high legal costs have been incurred, vast amounts of time have been expended by professional advisers and client on case preparation, and the parties' enthusiasm for litigation or arbitration has been completely sapped.

8.27   There are three main types of alternative dispute resolution: mediation, conciliation and the mini-trial.

MEDIATION
In mediation, an independent third party, the mediator, assists the parties through individual meetings with them ('caucuses') as well as joint sessions (a form of 'shuttle diplomacy') to focus on their real interests and strengths as opposed to their emotions in an attempt to draw them together towards possible settlement. The independent third party ordinarily does not make recommendations as to what would be an appropriate settlement; his role is to assist the parties to find a solution and reach agreement

themselves. The mediator is different from the adjudicator found in certain standard form contracts, who is called upon to make a decision.

CONCILIATION

The conciliator is usually less interventionist than the mediator but still endeavours to bring disputing parties together and to assist them to focus on the key issues. Conciliation has been well known in the United Kingdom in employment matters for a number of years via ACAS. Given the looseness of ADR terminology, the terms mediator and conciliator are often interchangeable.

MINI-TRIAL

In this approach each party presents the issues to senior executives of both parties, who are often assisted by a neutral chairman. The parties may, although not necessarily, be represented by lawyers. The chairman, perhaps a lawyer, may advise on the likely outcome of litigation without any binding authority on the parties. After presentation of the issues, the executives try to negotiate a settlement. If successful, the settlement is often set out in a legally enforceable written document. The mini-trial is a misnomer to the extent that it is not really a trial as such. With the legal rules of evidence usually discarded, it is a settlement procedure designed to convert a legal dispute back into a business problem. The mini-trial clearly has a number of advantages:

- a lengthy hearing is eliminated;
- each party's case can be professionally presented, but without any formal rules of procedure or evidence;
- those who ultimately decide whether the dispute should be settled (and on what terms) have the opportunity to be guided by a person with some degree of prestige and outside objectivity;
- the presentations are made to, and the ultimate decision made by, persons with the requisite authority to commit to settlement the bodies which they represent.

8.28   Since 1990, ADR has been promoted in the United Kingdom by a number of bodies, including the Centre for Dispute Resolution and the Chartered Institute of Arbitrators, with varying degrees of success. Construction professionals appear to be disillusioned with the conventional processes of litigation and arbitration: in the words of one former chairman of the Construction Industry Council:

'You can't win if you go to court. The high legal costs are part of it. Litigation is long and repetitive. The legal system is abysmal and inefficient.'

However, a sea change will be required in the culture of the construction industry before ADR is seen as little more than fringe medicine. Perhaps the construction industry is not yet ready for principled negotiations. Unfortunately the presentation of many contractor claims has now become something of a black art, with contractors gliding willingly to a position where they are taken in by the clever, often logically superficial, formulations of their own claims consultants. On the other side, many employers do not wish to pay or may have no money with which to pay. Arbitration or litigation then become equally attractive to both contractor and employer. The contractor believes that by means of a clever presentation he will be able to persuade a court or arbitrator of the legitimacy of his claim, while at the same time certain employers will view the slow and expensive legal process as a means of denying a contractor his legitimate and reasonable financial expectations.

8.29   In conclusion, all construction professionals must go back to basics and wonder whether or not the present procurement system is adequate. Is the traditional JCT-type contract now out-moded? Certainly it would appear that continental Europe, which adopts more of a construction management type approach, suffers fewer claims, although the same cannot be said of the United States which has been the prime promoter of the construction management system. It may simply be that English and American contractors are more litigious than their continental counterparts, but because the problems of the construction industry are so complex, the difficulties that arise during the course of contracts are more likely to have their origins in the whole procurement method, including the tendering process. Governmental awareness that all is not well with the world was reflected in the setting up of the inquiry under Sir Michael Latham into procurement and contractual arrangements in the UK construction industry. Now that his final report, *Constructing the Team*, is published it is time for solutions to be found – although was not the same said after the Banwell Report in 1964?

Table of cases

Peak Construction (Liverpool) Ltd v McKinney Foundations Ltd (1970)
1 BLR 1 (CA)

Perini Corporation Pty Ltd v Commonwealth of Australia (1969)
12 BLR 82 (Supreme Court of New South Wales)

President of India v La Pintada Compañía Navegacíon [1985]
AC 104 (HL)

R.W. Miller & Co Pty Ltd v Krupp (Australia) Pty Ltd (1992)
Unreported

Rees & Kirby Ltd v Swansea City Council (1985) 30 BLR 1 (CA)

Reigate v Union Manufacturing Co (Ramsbottom) Ltd and Elton Cop
Dyeing Company [1918] 1 KB 592 (CA)

Royal Borough of Kingston-upon-Thames v Amec Civil Engineering Ltd
(1993) 35 Con LR 39

Saint Line Ltd v Richardsons, Westgarth & Co Ltd [1940] 2 KB 99

Secretary of State for Transport v Birse Farr Joint Venture (1993)
35 Con LR 8

Shirlaw v Southern Foundries (1926) Ltd [1939] 2 KB 206 (CA)

Shui On Construction Ltd v Shui Kai Co Ltd (1985) 4 Const LJ 305
(Supreme Court of Hong Kong)

Stratton & Others v Inland Revenue Commissioners [1957]
2 All ER 594 (CA)

Sutcliffe v Thackrah and Others [1974] 4 BLR 16 (HL)

T.A. Bickerton & Son Ltd v North-West Metropolitan Regional Hospital
Board [1970] 1 WLR 607 (HL)

Tate & Lyle Food and Distribution Ltd v Greater London Council [1981]
3 All ER 717

Tersons Ltd v Stevenage Development Corporation (1963)
5 BLR 54 (CA)

The London, Chatham & Dover Railway Co v The South Eastern
Railway Co [1893] AC 429 (HL)

Trollope & Colls Ltd v North-West Metropolitan Regional Health Board
[1973] 9 BLR 60 (HL)

Victoria Laundry (Windsor) Ltd v Newman Industries Ltd [1949]
2 KB 528 (CA)

Wharf Properties Ltd and Wharf (Holdings) Ltd v Eric Cumine
Associates (No.2) (1991) 29 Con LR (PC)

Wells v Army & Navy Co-operative Society Ltd (1902) 86 LT 764

Wraight Ltd v P.H. & T. (Holdings) Ltd (1968) 13 BLR 26

Yorkshire Dale Steamship Company Ltd v Minister of War Transport
[1942] AC 691 (HL)

Index